Y0-BQC-486

Isometric Drills FOR STRENGTH AND POWER *in Athletics*

ISOMETRIC DRILLS

for Strength and Power

in ATHLETICS

by Fred Kelley

Parker Publishing Company, Inc., West Nyack, N.Y.

Library of Congress
Catalog Card Number: 66-29819

PRINTED IN THE UNITED STATES OF AMERICA

50639 — BC

DEDICATION

To My Wife, Sue

AND

Son, Michael

FOREWORD

It has become increasingly evident that being a top flight athlete is pretty much a year-round proposition. The great athletes in every sport work continuously not only to maintain, but to increase, symmetry, body strength or bulk. Toward the achievement of any or all of these ends, athletes and their coaches have adopted in great and growing numbers the isometric method of strength development.

Fred Kelley's book is a comprehensive delineation of the best procedures yet devised in the area of physical development.

These are tested and proven isometric exercises, clearly described, graphically illustrated by an accomplished athlete, and specifically oriented to particular muscle groups in addition to over-all body strength.

Coach Kelley has reached into his impressive background and training to develop this work, which is a true and accurate road map to Physical Betterment.

John McKenna
Former Head Football Coach, VMI
Now Assistant Athletic Director,
Georgia Tech

ACKNOWLEDGEMENTS

Appreciation is due to many of my friends and associates for their encouragement and help in preparing this book. My thanks to Coach John Bach of Fordham University, and Dr. Dean Foster of Virginia Military Institute for their helpful encouragement. Thanks also to Mrs. Janis Ayres, typist; Messrs. George Mohler and James Tillery, photographers; Coach Jack Reilly who posed for the photographs; and Mr. Pres Brown who contributed necessary equipment.

What Isometrics Can Mean to the Coach's Success

The coach who employs or wishes to employ isometrics in his program does so because he wants to provide his teams with the most efficient method of increasing the level of their physical condition, and maintaining this standard of strength and power throughout the season.

Most coaches interested in isometrics are saying this:

1. Give me a concise summary of the pertinent facts related to isometrics.
2. Give me a collection of proven exercises for various parts of the body.
3. Show me how to conduct and supervise these exercises intelligently so that the greatest possible benefit may be realized in the time available to me.
4. Provide me with aid in selecting those exercises which will be of direct benefit in *my* sport.
5. Show me an inexpensive method for evaluating the progress of my team members . . . not only for my own information, but to enable them to maintain a high degree of motivation.

This book will deal with each of these factors in turn, presenting to you in effect your own personal clinic on isometrics.

We will not go deeply into the physiological processes of muscular development . . . there are already excellent references available in this area. We will not be concerned with statistics . . . these are available in research reports. We will not extoll the virtues of the various gadgets and implements used in acquiring strength . . . reports are available if one has the time or the inclination to search them out. We *will* be concerned, however, with what a coach *needs* to know in order to initiate and conduct an effective isometric program, designed to provide an efficient, beneficial and inexpensive method of strength acquisition.

Exercises known to be of value in particular areas of athletics will be described and accompanied by clear photographs showing proper positioning and techniques. Along with the illustrations, details of proper execution are outlined, as an aid to the coach in helping the athlete reap the maximum benefit from the exercises.

For easy reference purposes, the book is arranged to cover the various areas of the body, enabling the coach to determine his athlete's problems and consult the appropriate chapter for a remedial program.

If your program is to be effective, provision must be made for evaluation and the book recognizes this need. The factors of budget, space, assistance, and time will be taken into account, and inexpensive but effective methods of evaluation will be outlined.

In short, this book was written with *you* in mind.

CONTENTS

CHAPTER ONE

Isometrics: A Strength-Building System

All coaches share a number of common experiences and revelations. One of the most important of these is the realization that very few boys come to us as "polished" athletes. Very early in our careers we recognize the fact that a varying amount of skill and capacity for learning may be present in an individual, but it remains the responsibility of the coach to shape, mold, and instruct the fledgling athlete. We accept this responsibility as the very basis of our duties.

Let's hypothesize for a moment. What would be the result in our programs if there were no attempt made to increase the level of a new player's intelligence and awareness? Suppose that we felt that we had to accept each individual as he came to us? Take football for instance. No blackboard sessions, no scrimmage experience, no individual instruction on the various types of blocks, defensive techniques, or any of the other intricacies of the game. We all know very well what would result. There *are* those who would not fare too badly, due to previous experience, agility, and coordination, but we realize that the average boy would not be a great deal of help to us on our squad. "Shocking," you say, "who would be so foolish as to assume that we could possibly field a team under these conditions?" Your reaction would be not only natural, but correct.

Now let's carry our hypothetical situation even further. Suppose that each of our players had an I.Q. of 160, walked ten miles to school every day, worked in the hay fields or on the loading playform of a cement company, abstained from alcohol and cigarettes, had no use for the weaker sex, worked all summer on a construction crew, and enjoyed a football scrimmage every day. Sounds great, doesn't it? We could really do something with raw material like this! Unfortunately, as we drift back down to earth from this lofty dream, we bump smack into the realization that most boys do not have the "opportunity" of engaging in many of these activities anymore, and thus we are once again faced with our usual material.

The sad fact of the matter is that all too many of us are ready to accept our physical raw material as it comes to us. In most cases this material is relatively soft, as a result of a life filled with automobiles and luxury conveniences. Although we wouldn't consider being content with our beginning players' initial mental state, we are satisfied with their physical frame. What an injustice to not only the boys, but ourselves! Our solution to the problem most of the time is to leave it to "mother nature," trusting that inches, pounds, and strength will be added to our athletes in due course. Is there a solution? I feel that there is, but before discussing it more fully, let's pause for a moment and consider the whole aspect of physical condition and strength in athletics.

Strength is necessary for effective performance in any athletic endeavor. There is some disagreement, however, as to how much strength is necessary, and how this quality should be obtained. Too many of us rely on the natural strength of the athlete, trusting in the actual participation in the sport to bring about conditioning. In this regard, consider some questions related to the three major sports and see if any of them apply to you or your athletes.

Football

Have you ever told one of your men that on a particular defensive set his only responsibility was to take a step in, whip the opposing end, then contain any sweeps? We hate to admit it to ourselves, but we realize that oftentimes no matter how much technique a boy possesses, he may be physically unable to defeat an opposing player. How many times have you told a back not to pussyfoot, but to run over a defender when he's inside the five yardline? It's a fairly simple statement to make, but what if the back does not possess the necessary drive in the legs or strength in the neck to allow him to simply lower his helmet and drive? Would you like to include deeper pass patterns in your offense, but are unable to do so because your quarterback is only able to throw the ball 30 yards with any speed? How many times in "cup protection" have you seen a lineman with good position and good technique get bowled over simply because he doesn't have the strength and bulk?

Basketball

Have you ever wondered why your six foot, nine inch center can go up and get the rebounds, but often loses the ball on the way down to a smaller man? How many times have you instructed your forwards and center not to allow themselves to be pushed around underneath the basket? How about your guard who has the fine outside shot during the first half, but becomes "arm weary" and is unable to come anywhere close to the basket the second half? Could you have your team employ a man-to-man press from the opening whistle and count on them to outlast the opposition?

Baseball

Have you ever had a big boy you could only use as a late reliever because his fastball simply lost its hop after three innings? Or a centerfielder who had all the range in the world defensively but was ineffective because of a weak arm? Have you ever had players who looked as though they should be pulling the ball with power, but were just punch hitters?

Today's Conditioning Methods

I feel sure that all of us have experienced similar situations relative to one of the sports mentioned. Your question now is probably "Yes, any one of these may be true, but what's to be done about it?" "What am I, as a coach, able to employ to remedy the situation?" My contention is that isometrics can play a large role in solving your conditioning problems.

One facet of our coaching profession that serves to bind its members together is the similarity of our problems. True, there are varying degrees of concern related to these problems, but most of us are interested in the restrictions imposed on our programs by time, space and budgetary considerations. With these problems in mind, let's look briefly at the methods available to us for conditioning today's athletes.

Isotonics

This form of strength acquisition has enjoyed a tremendous popularity in recent years. It is a system of training which employs the use of a resistance (weight) which is moved from one anatomical position to another. In short, any exercise in which a weight is moved is said to be isotonic in nature.

Isotonics is very valuable in athletics in that through the use of different and specific types of programs, varying results may be achieved. These programs will bring about weight reduction, strength, explosive power, endurance, and the addition of weight and mass.

The disadvantages of this form of training include the facts that a great deal of space is required to service an entire team; the purchase of proper equipment is costly; the employment of a comprehensive program requires a significant amount of time; and a well-run program requires close supervision at all times..

Calisthenics

Although there is certainly an incerase in strength in a conscientious program of calisthenics, the time required to perform enough repetitions of an exercise to produce this strength gain is almost prohibitive.

As far as the author is coincerned, calisthenics possess their greatest value as a warm-up activity.

Isometrics

Isometrics may be readily differentiated from isotonics in that whereas isotonics employ a *movable* resistance, isometrics makes use of an *immovable* one. Any object that cannot be displaced is a potential isometric resistance. The word isometric itself means literally "no change" or "no movement."

The techniques involved in this system will, of course, be dealt with fully in ensuing chapters.

Now let's explore isometrics a little more fully, relative to the problems and restrictions proposed previously in the chapter, and discover why the author feels that the inclusion of this system in a conditioning program can be one of the most efficient and expedient solutions to the problem of strength in athletics.

1. *Effectiveness*

Probably one of the most important advantages isometrics has is that of effectiveness. Numerous studies have been conducted and reported regarding this aspect, with the evidence in its effectiveness mounting with almost every inquiry. The results of those studies could be listed here, but instead of statistics, let me discuss some personal observations.

The author is probably as much of a "Missouri man" regarding new concepts as anyone reading this book. As a result, when I would peruse some of the claims made for isometrics I said "This I've got to see." Feeling that the best possible way to observe the effects of isometrics was to incomporate them in our program, we did.

Working with basketball players, and using a vertical jump apparatus as an indicator, I have observed individuals who increased their jumping ability 3⅝″. In this case, a six week program was conducted on the legs alone.

I have observed a baseball pitcher, on isometrics for eight weeks, exhibit a gain in weight from 165 pounds to 183 pounds, with a commensurate increase in bicep, chest, forearm and calf girth. Although the speed of his pitches was not measured scientifically, he continually reported an increase in speed and the ability to maintain it throughout nine innings.

After participation in our pre-season football program, we observed players exhibiting various increases in the size of that all-important area of the neck, the greatest increase being a jump from 15½″ to 17″. After observations of this type, I was highly pleased and gratified as I'm sure you will be as your labors begin to bear fruit.

2. *Time*

Time if one of our greatest restrictions in coaching. If we are to be effective, we must be assured that we are receiving the maximum benefits from any program we employ. Skull sessions, movie reviews, and the necessary instruction in fundamentals occupy the lion's share of the pre-season time allotment. Our conditioning program then, cannot be allowed to occupy the one and one-half to two hours, three times per week required in an isotonic type of program. Isometrics, however, fill the bill admirably. The same quality of strength is produced in a mere fraction of the time. Even during the season, when pressure becomes more evident, we can continue with a once-per-week schedule, secure in the knowledge that we are *increasing* the level of strength which has been attained in the pre-season program. Even a portion of a boy's lunch hour may be utilized for exercising during the season. When one realizes that an entire football team may be run through a comprehensive program in twenty to twenty-five minutes, it becomes evident that isometrics can be one of our strongest allies in our fight against the clock.

3. *Space*

Here is another one of our limiting factors in the average coaching situation. The problem assumes greater magnitude when we consider that most of our pre-season conditioning programs are conducted during the time when other sports are in season. This of course means that much of the indoor space normally available is occupied by the current sport. With space at a premium, it is virtually impossible to employ a conditioning program involving isotonics or calisthenics. On the other hand, isometrics may be utilized in a very limited space, even that encompassed by the average-sized room .With proper organization, a squad of 45 members may exercise in a space no larger than a normal classroom. An additional advantage is that all of the equipment necessary for a workout travels with you. If you were to use two-man isometrics in a program for example, they could actually be done on the field before practice sessions or games.

4. *Budget*

Most coaches in an average situation are unable to afford the great capital outlay necessary to install a fully-equipped weight room, with the result that the idea of building strength in a pre-season program is either neglected altogether or consists of agility drills and calisthenics.

A full scale program of isometrics, on the other hand, may be instituted with a very small amount of cash and the assistance of the school shop. Although there are fine commercial devices on the market, imagination and handy materials will still provide the coach with the necessary tools to initiate a beneficial program. Wood stock combined with a metal bar, lengths of rope, or even the body itself will suffice in an isometric program. It has been the author's experience in many cases that when the powers that be who control the purse strings observe the resulting benefits of a program that has been begun and maintained on a shoestring, they may tend to be more receptive to the desires of a coach when appropriation time rolls around again.

5. *Administrative Ease*

Once a concise lecture has been presented and the participants are aware of the principles involved and the techniques to be employed, an isometric program virtually runs itself. Although any good isotonic program is relatively safe, there is never any question of injury resulting from isometrics. This knowledge will allow the coach to delegate a number of his managerial or training staff to supervise the program, while utilizing his own time for other duties.

6. *Injury Rehabilitation*

In most situations when an athlete is injured, his practice time is spent in street clothing, assisting in the mechanics of a practice session. For example, if a halfback sprains an ankle severely, you will most likely find him on the sidelines holding the down marker or the chains. This is not the place for an athlete. Of course, the boy should be receiving physiotherapy, but even this is not enough. Not only does the muscle tonicity in the injured appendage suffer from atrophy, but the level of fitness of the individual as a whole deteriorates. With isometrics, a boy need not waste away in the two to three weeks of recuperation. He can be put on a remedial program involving not only the unaffected portions of his body, but may even do selective isometric exercises involving musculature in the injured appendage. This practice will bring a boy back to participation at a higher level of readiness and effectiveness.

One word of caution. As we have indicated, the advantages of an isometric system of training are numerous, but remember this. Isometrics should be considered a supplement. The system should not be thought of as a panacea in athletics. Isometrics by itself will not turn your losing seasons into winning ones, nor your lap dog athletes into snarling mastiffs.

We all have reached the conclusion by this time that there is an X factor involved in athletics that defies intelligent explanation. This intangible has sometimes been called intestinal fortitude, or simply guts. Without it a boy may possess all the necessary physical equipment and still remain woefully impotent as an effective performer. If it were possible to attach a few electrodes to a prospective athlete, punch a button causing a needle to point to a number signifying the amount of this X factor present, our recruiting budgets would be much smaller, and our nights would probably be much more restful.

We might as well agree on the fact that our coaching techniques, personalities, the natural rate of maturation of a boy, and a little social pressure may have *some* effect in this area, but when considered in the light of over-all performance their value is almost negligible. No, isometrics should not be considered the long-sought solution to all of our coaching problems. What is it then? I believe the concept to be the most valuable supplement to intelligent coaching and administration known to us today.

SUMMARY

In short, it is obvious that we need a method of developing strength in athletes prior to the commencement of the competitive season, and maintaining this level throughout its duration.

The employment of isometrics is one of the most feasible, efficient and effective methods of solving the problem.

CHAPTER TWO

Isometrics Simplified

The fact that most of us approach any new principle or idea with a certain amount of mistrust is in keeping with our human nature. Most of us are happier if someone else tries a new system out first, allowing us to make adjustments and observations of their success or failure with it.

I feel it would be safe to say that many times this attitude is a result of a lack of knowledge on our part, concerning the basic principles involved in the system. We are usually dubious of the unknown, and therefore reluctant to incorporate a new theory or procedure into our routine, even though it may be of great value to us.

So it is, I believe, with isometrics. This chapter has been included in order to answer some of the most common questions proposed by coaches. The answers may help to provide a broader knowledge of the basics included in isometrics, enabling the reader to make an intelligent evaluation of his needs and his program.

Keeping these principles in mind, the coach should be better equipped to initiate an intelligent, worth-while program of isometrics in the total conditioning procedure.

What is an isometric contraction?

An isometric contraction is one in which the muscles contract against an immovable resistance. The immobility of the resistance produces a tremendous amount of tension within the muscle itself. This resistance could consist of any object too heavy to move; a rope, an iron bar, or the opposing parts of the body itself.

What is the principle involved in isometrics?

The basic principle of isometrics is that if a muscle is contracted once a day for six seconds, at two-thirds of its maximum power, that muscle will increase significantly in size and strength.

This fact is very difficult for us to understand, or at least accept, because for so long in this country we have been exposed to what has sometimes been called the "sweat complex." The complex is based on the theory that in order for us to derive any benefit from a workout, a great deal of time must be expended.

We have all been exposed to, and participated in, this type of conditioning. We had to go to the gymnasium or playing field, change clothing, spend an hour or more in activity until a great amount of perspiration was forthcoming, return for a shower, and look forward in the morning upon arising to a collection of minor aches and pains. We have all heard the old adage that an exercise is not doing us any good until it hurts.

The author certainly does not mean to imply that perspiration and arduous training has no place in conditioning. My point is that there is room for other types of conditioning in our programs.

Returning to the basic question here, I feel that in order to derive any benefit through the use of isometrics, the users must be made to believe the fact that the principle of isometrics is a sound, scientifically proven truth.

How was this principle developed?

Actually, the principle was discovered quite by accident. While working on an experiment unrelated to isometrics, the researchers found it necessary to use a frog with one leg bound to a board while the other one was allowed to function freely. In the course of the experiment, the frog was subjected to muscular stimulation, causing a series of muscle jerks. As the procedure progressed, it became evident to the scientists that the leg which was encumbered became visibly larger than the free leg. This fact of course resulted in speculation as to why this was so, . . . and the theory of isometrics was born.

Why weren't isometrics used widely in athletics until a short time ago?

The answer goes back to the introduction of this chapter. Basically, there is a normal resistance to any change, especially in a field such as ours in which experience and word-of-mouth information plays a large role.

Since isometrics were not available to most of the coaches active today during their competing years, it was naturally felt that there was nothing wrong with the old system of preparing for competition. This feeling was basically well-founded, if we stop to consider the era in which the system was developed. Here again we must take into consideration the fact that the normal activities of the athletes in those days were of the type that contributed to increasing strength. The walking, the shovelling, the carrying of coal and ice, and the work on the farm were all ready-made methods of getting into, and staying in good physical condition.

Today we need an artificial method of strength acquisition, and isometrics provides us with just such a device.

How long should an isometric contraction be held?

Although the law of isometrics states that a contraction should be of six seconds duration, there are justifiable reasons why the contraction should be held for a longer period.

Many experiments have been conducted on this particular portion of the isometric principle, and it has been demonstrated that if contractions are sustained for periods of time less than six seconds, the maximum benefits expected from a contraction will not result. On the other hand, it has been proven that contractions of any greater length of time than six seconds do not produce any commensurate increase in strength when compared to those held for only six seconds. This much is fact.

The author feels a contraction should be held no less than eight or nine seconds. If an athlete is told that he must contract for six seconds at a given intensity, in most cases he will attempt to reach this stage too quickly, possibly causing a strain on the muscle. If, on the other hand, he is allowed to gradually increase the intensity of contraction over a span of two to three seconds, he will reach the desired stage more safely and comfortably. Once this level is reached, of course, the contraction should be held for an additional six full seconds.

What should the intensity of a contraction be?

As we have stated previously in this chapter, the optimum intensity of contraction which will produce the most ideal results, need only be two-thirds of the possible maximum. This fact has been proven experimentally, and no objection to its validity is made here.

Unfortunately, most people literally do not know their own strength, and herein lies a problem. If any of the performers are a trifle lazy by nature, and have been told to contract at two-thirds maximum, the actual level attained may be below that desired.

For this reason, I feel that better results are obtained if the participants are instructed to contract at their maximum. As has been proposed previously, the maximum should be attained gradually over a period of two or three seconds. In this way, as he strives for his maximum, the athlete will have achieved the two-thirds level necessary to satisfy the requirements of the isometric principle.

It should be noted here that verbal encouragement can play a large role in persuading the participant to contract maximally.

How many positions should be used for each exercise?

The basic principle of isometrics provides us with no guidelines to follow, allowing us to exercise our individuality and inventiveness.

It is my contention that at least two, and ideally three positions should be used for each exercise. Let's take an example. If the biceps brachii was the muscle with which we were concerned, we would have to admit that the arms are not always flexed to the same degree during movements in athletics. This should indicate to us that the muscle had to be strong through its whole range of motion, and if such is true, *developed* throughout its range.

Consequently, I contend that in using a *curling* exercise in an attempt to develop these biceps, the positions used should approximate a near-extension position, a partially-flexed position, and a near-fully flexed position. In doing so, the muscle fibers are allowed to contract at varying degrees of flexion.

It might also be noted that rather than keeping the position of the bar or isometric device in the same position each workout period for a particular phase of an exercise, the performers should be encouraged to vary the placement of the bar slightly to allow even greater latitude in developmental range.

How many weeks should be allowed for an isometric program?

Here again we are given an opportunity in creating a

specially designed program for our own particular situation. Guidelines have been developed by research which enable us to set up a program to suit our particular needs. Let's look at a concept we should keep in mind when scheduling our isometric conditioning program in relation to our competitive season.

It is a scientifically proven fact that the length of time we retain a newly-acquired strength level is in direct proportion to the rate at which it was gained. In other words, if we develop strength through a four week program, at the end of an additional four weeks, the new strength will begin to decrease.

Bearing this in mind, I would suggest that a longer period than four weeks be used. It has been my experience that a six to eight week period of isometrics produces the best result. It allows our athletes to compete during the whole of almost any athletic season at their peak strength.

If time or circumstances do not permit a four week program, however, try to begin the program at the earliest possible date prior to the competition season.

Should isometrics be continued into the season?

This is an area in which isometrics enjoys a tremendous advantage over isotonics. Because of the amount of time required in using an isotonic program, it is virtually impossible to continue a training program once the season has begun. That is not the case with isometrics. If only ten or fifteen minutes a day are available, a beneficial program of constant conditioning may still be maintained.

The next logical question concerns the necessity for a conditioning program after the commencement of the competitive season. Is it really needed? I feel it is.

Is it true that the normal participation in practices and contests will keep a boy in the peak physical condition? I don't believe so. Even though we incorporate calisthenics and warm-ups as a matter of routine, and even though we try our best to have everyone engaged in some activity during a practice session, it is not always feasible. Keep in mind that we are also concerned here with the decrease in strength level due to a time lapse. For these reasons, I feel that a diminished program of isometrics during the competitive season is highly desirable. The number of days the program is used may be decreased to two workouts per week, still allowing the athlete to maintain his acquired strength level. This brings up the following question.

How many days a week should be devoted to isometrics?

If we are concerned here simply with the rapid acquisition of strength, then probably a five-day per week program would be the answer. Some additional considerations should be included however.

No one likes to do the same thing day after day. Interest lags and performances become lax. This is especially true if the program is to be conducted over an eight week period. Therefore, I feel that an alternate-day type of program would yield the best results in the long run. Over an extended period the difference in strength gain would be negligible, but at the same time you would achieve higher interest and better performances.

Another important factor is that the human body requires rest. Strength is acquired more readily if there are provisions for reduction or complete absence of activity for short periods during the conditioning process. These periods might be called "growth periods", during which the chemical processes of muscular change may take place, unhampered by strenuous activity.

What is the "overload principle"?

The overload principle is the basis for all types of resistance training, be it isotonic or isometric. The principle states that a muscle will not gain in size or strength unless it is subjected to increasingly heavier loads. If one were using isotonics, either the weight used would have to be increased periodically, or the number of repetitions accomplished would have to be raised.

How do we accomplish this adherence with isometrics? If we draw a parallel between isotonic and isometric training, we would have to compare the weights used in isotonic exercises to the muscular force applied to the resistance in isometric training. We have been told that this muscular force should be our maximums each time we contract. Through the process of gaining a small amount of strength each time we exercise, the maximum force we are concerned with becomes greater. Instead of adding extra weight to the resistance, as we would in isotonics, we are adding to the force of contraction we apply to the resistance. Thus, we are subjecting the muscle to increasingly heavier loads, and adhering to the principle.

What is oxygen debt?

The term is used to describe the condition which seems to be responsible for the increase in strength in a muscle. For reasons which are still being determined by scientists, when muscle fibers are deprived of a sufficient supply of oxygen, they tend to increase in strength and size.

In isotonic exercises the phenomenon occurs toward the last repetitions performed in a set, after the muscle fibers have been fatigued through constant repetition with sufficient weight.

In isometrics, the oxygen debt occurs to almost all muscle

fibers during a six second contraction at two-thirds maximum power. For this reason, it is extremely important to carry the contraction through for the *full* six seconds, and to make sure that at least two-thirds of the maximum power is being used. If this is not the case, then only a fraction of the total number of fibers contained in a muscle may be affected and the best possible results would not be achieved.

Is there any danger involved in isometrics?

Periodically, during the last few years, critics of isometrics have received publicity relative to their denunciations of the system and its effects. Usually these reports deal with the charge that isometrics are injurious to the heart, joints, ligaments, tendons, muscles or indeed, all of these. For many years, until research proved differently, there was a tremendous hue and cry against all athletics in general on the grounds that if anyone participated in strenuous activity, they would develop the so-called "athlete's heart." Research subsequently proved that since the heart was a muscle, and as such had the ability to hypertrophy, the result of exercise which caused it to function beyond the extent required by normal activity was actually beneficial, and not detrimental. Greater size allowed the organ to function more slowly and efficiently. Thus, the critics were silenced.

The author does not mean to imply that there is no danger at all involved in isometrics. In our profession we are dealing with activities everyday that could produce injury if not carefully supervised. So it is with any system of conditioning. It is possible, through improper preparation, to *pull* muscles in almost any activity, and in fact, in those which are not even strenuous in nature. We have to be as careful in the use of isometrics as in any form of conditioning or athletic activity. Let's review some of the comments made relative to isometrics and evaluate them.

Vertigo Sensation

Some users of isometrics complain that while holding a maximum contraction for the designated period, they experience a sensation of vertigo. This is not due to the fact that a maximum effort is being expended, but rather that most individuals tend to hold their breath throughout the contraction. For some participants it is perfectly all right, but for others, the forced closing of the epiglottis creates the Valsalva effect, causing them to feel dizzy and light-headed. Most of us either saw, or experienced the effect ourselves as youngsters, when one boy would stand behind another, have him take a deep breath and hold it, then wrap his arms about the breath-holder, and squeeze. This type of highly dangerous action would produce the same result. How can it be combatted? If I have participants who are overly subject to this; I instruct them to breathe in quick, short gasps throughout the contraction. This type of breathing will relieve the pressure which produces the effect. A maximum effort is still the result.

Too Much Force

Some critics have said that isometric exercises are too forceful for the joints of the body. They claim that the tremendous pressure resulting from isometric contraction is injurious. Have you ever noticed (in slow motion) the forces which come to bear on the human body during a football, baseball or basketball game? I include almost all sports in this category because these forces are not confined to contact sports alone. Let's face it gentlemen; we are not dealing in our profession with the average boy.

Look at the populations of your representative high schools

or colleges and see what percentage is composed of athletes. The figures will vary, but I doubt that in many cases the percentage be large. And just what is it we're trying to do with this percentage through isometrics? We are attempting to prepare them physically to go out onto the field, court or diamond and take part in an activity that involves running, stopping and starting quickly, changes of direction at full speed, collisions, falling, jumping, twisting and just about every movement of which the human body is capable. Isn't it more sensible to condition the musculature surrounding these joints in question with a gradual, intelligent developmental program so that the forces involved in athletic activity can be tolerated? Or should we trust to luck that calisthenics or some other milder form of conditioning will suffice to prevent injury? My contention is that if our bodies are going to be subjected to tremendous stresses, we ought to prepare them, and I don't feel this can be accomplished by a "half-way" conditioning program.

Muscle Strains

What about muscle strains? As was stated previously, it is possible to strain a muscle in almost any activity, be it rigorous or mild. The need to prepare correctly for physical exercise is probably the best answer here. In addition, if we look at the nature of isometrics, we will find that it enjoys an advantage over other forms of conditioning relative to muscle strain, in that if at any time a muscle does not feel "right" as we are performing, all that is required to remedy the situation is to release the resistance. This is not possible in weight training, for example. If one is attempting to press a particular weight and a muscular cramping or "catch" develops, we are hard-pressed (no pun intended) to release the weight safely.

The fact that we are encouraged to build up to a maximum contraction over a short period of time in isometrics is also an advantage. In effect, we are actually warming up as a part of the exercise.

Heart Strain

How about strain on the heart? Practically all that need be said about isometrics in this regard is the fact that isometric training would have to be classed as a vigorous activity, comparable to participation in most sports. If a person is medically fit to participate in athletics, then isometrics will not harm him any more than playing a contest would.

Will isometrics increase endurance?

Although of late there have been reports that some favorable indications have been observed in this area, at the present time the answer would have to be that for our purposes they do not.

In order for endurance to be increased, a repetitive type of activity must be used. For example, many repetitions performed with a small weight isotonically. With this system, a process of capillarization occurs, allowing more oxygen and blood to be brought to a working muscle, and more waste materials transported away. Capillarization cannot be said to occur to any great extent in isometrics.

Does exercising at different times on workout days have any effect?

It has been proved that a varying schedule of exercise time has no appreciable effect on results. There are, however, some considerations to keep in mind.

If a rigid time schedule is set up for workouts, some coaches feel that better success is obtained. Athletes know exactly when they are to condition, and these coaches feel that they exhibit a greater degree of mental preparedness. Other coaches, (including the author) feel that flexibility in the schedule will allow the athlete to exercise when he is feeling most fit. The final decision rests with the individual coach on this matter.

Keep in mind too, that in order for the exercises to bear fruit, the contraction has to be of a certain degree. If the athlete is tired or not well, his two-thirds maximum will not be as intense as his normal contraction.

How many times a day should a participant exercise?

One workout per day will produce the same results as multiple exercise periods. However, because of time limitations, a coach might want to set up a schedule whereby a boy conditioned a particular portion of the body during one session, and a different portion the next.

For best results, however, one workout period per day is sufficient.

Is the quality of strength produced through isometrics the same as that gained through isotonics?

The answer is yes. No difference in the quality of the strength gained through these two different forms has ever been observed. In fact, the length of retention of a newly acquired strength level is essentially the same with both methods due to the fact that although dissimilar in many respects, they both adhere to the principle that overload and oxygen debt is responsible for the increase in strength produced.

What about becoming "muscle bound" through the use of isometrics?

Stop and think for a moment about a definition for this term. Although we hear it used frequently, most of us find it difficult to attach a succinct meaning to the phrase. Let's assume that what we mean by "muscle bound" is a decrease in the range of motion in the joints. This being the case, we would simply have to work the joint through its full range of motion as we exercise, making sure that whenever we contract a particular muscle, we also extend that same muscle and the joint with which it's associated.

For this reason, I recommend a program of stretching and flexion after an isometric workout, topped off by a full-arm hang from the isometric bar, held for ten to fifteen seconds. This will allow all of the muscle fibers contracted during the exercise bout to be stretched and aligned.

Does an isometric program have any value in rehabilitating athletes?

It certainly does. Its value is two-fold. We all know that the quadriceps femoris is one of the fastest muscle groups in the human body to atrophy, probably due to the fact that we use them so much in everyday activities. All of us have seen the tremendous wasting away of the muscle as a leg is confined to a cast for any length of time. It has been proven that a single isometric contraction per day will retard this atrophy. The contraction, of course, may be done right inside the cast, as long as it does not aggravate the injury.

Secondly, if a boy is injured in a practice session or in a game, we usually give him physiotherapy and then, if the injury is a sprained ankle or injured knee, relegate him to the job of holding the down markers or plotting defenses. While this period of inactivity is healing the injury, it is also contributing to a breakdown of his over-all condition. Through the use of isometrics, a boy with an injured limb may still maintain his condition. If need be, he may even sit while performing his exercises. Here again is an advantage of isometrics over many other forms of conditioning.

When should results of an isometric program be expected to occur, and will they be the same for everyone?

Evidences of the results of a program should begin to appear after a period of about two weeks, depending on the evaluation methods being utilized.

The same results will not be common to all of the participants, however. This is only logical, since we know that some of the athletes are closer to their true strength potential than others. For those boys who are not so well developed, the effects will probably be greater and more noticeable at the outset, then they will begin to taper off and fall closer to the advancement of the rest of the group. This fact should be explained to the team and emphasized periodically. Otherwise, if we should constantly congratulate only those who are demonstrating rapid strides in development, the athletes who were at a higher level in the beginning would begin to feel that they were not making progress, and begin to lose interest. By all means, guard against this.

SUMMARY

Many coaches have been unaware of the basic simplicity of an isometric system of training and have refrained from incorporating it into their overall developmental regimens.

This chapter has attempted to answer the most common questions of concern to those responsible for the establishment of the conditioning program.

Because isometrics are fairly young in their application to our programs, a good deal of conjecture surrounds the answers to many specific inquiries concerning their use. The answers to the questions dealt with previously in this chapter have, in the main, been scientifically proven through intelligent research, and will provide a solid foundation on which the coach may design and build his program.

CHAPTER THREE

Selecting Your Conditioning Program

Importance of Personnel Selection

One basic principle adhered to by most coaches is that of "fitting the system to the personnel." We might wish to employ the single wing for example, but to enjoy any great success with it using 150 pound linemen and 130 pound backs would seem most improbable. In basketball, the shuffle offense is a winning system for some coaches, but with slow inside men and short guards, the plan loses its effectiveness. In short, although we might prefer to utilize a specific system, our personnel should govern our final selection.

The principle of proper selection must carry over into our conditioning programs. All too often, it is not the case, resulting in dissatisfaction on the part of both the coach and the athlete.

Many times in the discussion of isometric and weight training programs with coaches, I have been told that although a program had been initiated and the performers very faithful in their participation in it, the results fell far short of those desired. Failure in the achievement of success may usually be traced to a number of factors, most of which may be corrected in a simple manner. In many cases, the coach continues using the same uncorrected program for another year, then gives up entirely on the idea of isometrics or weight training in the conditioning program. One cannot really blame the coach either, since in many instances an improperly selected program may even prove to be a liability to its users, rather than an asset.

Use of Borrowed Programs

Why not use an established, pre-set type of conditioning program? Suppose that a professional or collegiate team in the area has been utilizing isometrics in their program. Let's assume that the staff of the particular school is willing to disseminate the information regarding their exercises, methods and techniques. More important, suppose that their team has been enjoying great success in the win column. Why not jot down some notes on the operation of the program and initiate the same one in your own situation? The spade work has already been accomplished for you, and you won't have to be plagued by the trial and error system. Why not?

Pursuit of this line of reasoning has led many coaches to the establishment of an ill-advised, ill-suited program of conditioning for their athletes.

Let's examine a few of the reasons why the use of a borrowed program might not produce the desired results.

Age Differential

One of the most apparent reasons for a possible lack of success is the factor of the ages of the athletes utilizing a particular program. We all recognize that in most sports there is a wide variance of ability between the performances of professional, collegiate and high school athletes. I will grant that a portion of the difference may be due to the experience aspect, but I feel a larger percentage is due simply to the fact that strength potential at one age is not what it is at a more advanced age. Different areas of the body should be emphasized at differing stages of development. For example, a professional baseball pitcher, as a result of long years of practice and participation, would need less emphasis placed on the development of the flexors and extensors of the wrist, than would a neophyte of 15 or 16 years of age. Whereas the younger athlete should be concentrating more on strength, the professional might be more interested in muscular tonicity and endurance. This factor should account for differing programs.

Environment Differential

Here again is an area that should play a role in our selection of a program and should provide us with an additional factor to consider in the acceptance of a program designed by other coaches.

In most cases in high school, little control may be exercised over environmental factors. We put our boys in training, but in the final analysis it is the athlete's family that controls the dietary, sleep, and recreational factors.

This is not the case in most colleges or in the professional realm of athletics however. When a boy has shown sufficient skill to be included on a squad, he will be assigned to a training table, where his diet may be strictly controlled. The bill of fare will include those foods which have been proven to be beneficial in the development of good health and body building essentials. In many other instances the athlete may also be assigned to an athletic dormitory, where training rules may be closely supervised. Similar supervision would be all but impossible on the high school level.

In professional athletics of course, the training habits of an athlete are even more closely supervised.

Time Element

This is a factor that again may be overlooked when we consider using someone else's program. Some of these programs are set up on a more elaborate scale than we could possibly employ in a particular situation. The time factor depends on class load, whether or not you are involved in a rural or urban school, the size of the staff available, and other considerations. Consequently, one school may have up to twice as much time for a conditioning program as another.

Specialization

Specialization in athletics is a luxury that most of our programs do not permit us to enjoy. In the professional ranks of a sport such as football, we have the kickoff team, the receiving team, the goal-line defensive team, and so on. It would be a simple matter to develop conditioning programs for these players, since their activities cover such a narrow spectrum. A program designed for a pro team would hardly be suited to a high school or even college. In these cases, we are utilizing players who must go *two ways*, and whose conditioning must cover a greater range than professionals.

Steps in Selecting Your Program

Examination of the Present Physical Condition of the Athlete

At the outset it should be pointed out to the coach initiating a conditioning program that nothing should be taken for granted. Do not assume that your team members, since they are a certain chronological age, should approximate a certain level of strength. Difference in growth rate, basic health habits and other factors all contribute toward making this assumption a fallacy. If we are to establish a system of conditioning which will benefit *each* of our players, then each of our players must be considered initially.

One excellent method of determining the health and fitness level that each of our players has attained is the examination of records. I would suggest that the inspection of two types of records would afford the coach a fairly accurate picture of the health and physical fitness status of the athlete. These are the school medical examination records, and the physical fitness test cards.

1. *Medical Examination*

Since it is standard procedure in most schools to administer annual health and physical examinations, we have at our disposal a ready-made yardstick to use in our evaluation of the thlete. The record indicates the answers to many questions which should be of interest to the coach. Does the boy's weight fluctuate greatly from period to period? Does he have dental problems which could contribute to low weight? Is he highly susceptible to colds and infectious diseases? Has he any congenital physical infirmities which may not be evident in a cursory examination? What is his history regarding nausea, frequent headaches and shortness of breath? The answer to all these questions and more should show the general health condition of our prospective athletes.

2. *Physical Fitness Test Results*

Just as health examinations are standard procedure in most schools today, so it is with physical fitness testing. The test may be as simple as a push-up, pull-up and running type, or may be as involved as a Rogers P.F.I. Test, but in most school systems today some type of procedure is ordinarily employed. If this is not the case in your situation, then I would strongly advise that the coaching staff compile and administer one.

It is fairly evident what indications may be garnered from the inspection of these records. How does the boy stand in relation to national norms established for his height, weight and age? What are his strongest areas? More important, which are his weakest? The answers to these questions should provide you with an intelligent basis for determining the needs of individual players.

What Type of Conditioning is Needed?

The next step to consider in selecting a program is so obvious that it is often overlooked entirely. If you do not answer this question, you are proceeding blindly. Different types of conditioning programs yield different results. If you choose the wrong type initially, then all that follows is wasted effort.

There are three primary types of conditioning programs.

1. *Endurance*

If endurance is your major consideration, then you should employ a system of training isotonically in which relatively light weights are used, coupled with a high number of repetitions.

2. *Explosive Power*

Explosive power is the aspect of strength defined as expending a tremendous amount of energy in a short period of time such as putting the shot. If this type of strength is needed in a particular sport, then your conditioning program should include the use of medium weights, a medium number of repetitions with a concentration on the speed of the repetitions.

3. *Strength*

Strength is the primary area in which isometrics can play an important role. Isotonics may be employed using heavy weights, low repetitions and multiple sets, but isometrics can carry the bulk of the load in this area.

With the knowledge of these types of programs in mind, it remains for the coach to look at his sport or activity and establish which area is of prime importance. If strength is one of the objectives, then isometrics should definitely be included in the program.

Examination of Gross Muscle Movement

After the primary determination is made that strength is needed, the next logical consideration is . . . where? This too is an extremely important decision, in that a great deal of time and effort may be wasted if participants in the program are required to concentrate on areas of the body or musculature which play little or no role in the activity.

The answer to this question can be gained from books and established programs, but if a program is to be truly tailor-made, then the individual coach should make the selection.

Ideally, the task will be made much easier if each man possessed a background in kinesiology and/or physiology. Since this is not often the case, the use of the "coach's eye" can be of extreme value. What is "coach's eye"? To me, it is the ability to visualize correct procedure in my mind; to have a mental picture of an action. We put it to use every day on the practice field, diamond, or court. Through experience and the ability to visualize proper techniques in our minds, we know when a boy is coming up too quickly on a start, or dipping a shoulder in a swing. "Coach's eye" is an extremely valuable tool of our trade.

How do we use it here? In a selection for football, it might work something like this. We put our feet upon the desk, lean back, close our eyes and say to ourselves, "Football." "How do you play the game?" "You run that way, come off your stance, that way, throw a ball that way, forearm shiver that way, scramble block that way, etc." The next step is to lock the office door so no one will think that you've finally gone off the deep end, and actually go through these motions. Feel around and probe yourself a little as you do. Determine what parts of your body are functioning in performing these movements. As you do, you will actually be selecting the areas of the body that need concentration in your program. Once you establish these, you're off and running toward a successful program.

Subtle Movements

Once the major musculature utilized in the basic movements of the sport have been analyzed and selected, you should carry the procedure a bit further to include these actions carried out by specialists or men in particular positions. These might include passers, punters, place kickers, pulling guards, punt protectors, etc. Once the same procedure has been followed for the actions involved in these particular movements and techniques, place your results on a separate list. Concentration on these areas of the body and this particular musculature may be accomplished through supplemental or specialized programs performed only by those to whom they apply. In this manner, while your linemen are concentrating on the basic program performed by all personnel, the others may be concentrating on specialized areas of the body. These supplemental exercises should be included in the program over and above the basic exercises.

The incorporation of an analyze and choose type of procedure will aid in the establishment of a program designed specifically for your personnel.

Simplicity

Many otherwise beneficial programs have been undone by the fact that too much complexity was involved in the exercises. If a high level of interest is to be maintained, the program must be established on a simple basis. The reason for the inclusion of each exercise should be readily understood by each performer, as should the technique of performance. If elaborate procedures must be made for each exercise, more time will be spent in preparation than in participation which will decrease a performer's interest in the exercise and the program.

Number of Exercises

The number of exercises will also contribute to the success or failure of a program. Those included should cover the prime areas and musculature effectively, but should not be so numerous that the program bogs down under the sheer amount of them. It has been my experience that if boys are given too many exercises in a program, they become concerned with the inclusion of all of them and the accomplishment of the entire regimen. Individual exercises are often rushed and performed so hastily that in the end effectiveness and quality have been sacrificed for quantity.

For most sports, a program containing 9-12 exercises to be

performed in a single session produces the best results. By this, I certainly do not mean to say that only 9 basic exercises should be performed for a sport. Rather, specific exercises may be included in one session and excluded in another in favor of additional ones.

SUMMARY

As has been indicated, selection of your exercises is one of the most important facets of the entire program. A little extra effort and time spent in choosing them at the outset will reap tremendous benefits later on.

Do not be satisfied with someone else's program. Build your own. As you do, you will gain valuable knowledge which will serve you in good stead should the need arise to modify the program at a later date. The program will mean a lot more to your athletes if you have a ready, intelligent answer to their questions as to why you are including a particular exercise or why they should perform it in a specific manner, rather than if your only available response is that "Podunk U. does it that way."

One more point in conclusion. The field of isometrics, although relatively old in theory, is young in application. Not all the exercises which it is possible to perform are recorded somewhere. My point is this. Don't be afraid of experimentation! If you have an athlete who does not perform a particular movement in sports in the classic, accepted manner, devise an exercise of your own for him. The point to remember is: Oppose the action. *For example, if the musculature you are concerned with serves to pull the arm forward, devise an exercise that closely approximates the actual movement to be made, with the isometric bar or restraining device preventing that movement from being accomplished.*

Remember, any *exercise is a good one if it works.*

CHAPTER FOUR

Organization and Supervision of the Program

Often we have heard that a particular coach is a fine teacher, or that he has a fine technical mind, or is a great fundamentalist, or is an excellent organizer and administrator. Of all of these facets involved in being a good coach, one which is extremely important is often left to chance. I am referring now to organization.

Facts concerning formations and strategy are ones to which we are constantly exposed. Most clinics we attend are oriented toward this area. No one is disputing the point that we would certainly be remiss in our preparation for coaching if we did not possess technical knowledge. On the other hand, the ability to organize and dispense our information in an effective manner is one that must be either inherent or learned if we are to utilize our facts and techniques correctly. This chapter will assist the coach in the organization of a conditioning program so that time and personnel will be employed to the best advantage.

Orientation to the Program

Orientation is an area frequently passed over lightly but which may spell success or failure in our programs. The need for proper orientation to any new program cannot be stressed too strongly. In the final analysis, it may be reduced to a single factor: If a boy knows *why* he is required to perform a function, he will accomplish that function more effectively, and with higher interest. I have observed isometric programs being conducted in which the only prior instruction conveyed to the athletes was that he was supposed to "grab that bar this way and pull on it until told to stop." Little wonder that such a program seldom achieves any great popularity or success.

Isometrics is strange and new to most participants. The action of simply contracting against an immovable object is one that is easy to perform, but very difficult to grasp. Boys are competitive by nature. If they have been exposed to any sort of organized conditioning program in the past, it was probably one in which weights were used. Ah . . . here was something they could sink their teeth into! A chance to prove that they could lift more than the other man who was the same height and weight as they. Now we tell him that all this has been changed. As he looks around him while exercising isometrically, he knows that he is certainly applying more force than that small boy next to him, yet both of their isometric bars are not moving. Why is this doing him any good? He certainly deserves an explanation. How may we best prepare him for effective participation in an isometric program? Let's look at the steps which should be folowed.

The Initial Meeting

The first important step is to call the entire team together for a meeting. The assembly should include any one even remotely connected with the athletic team in season. Managers, trainers, team physicians, athletic directors and any other individuals who share in the responsibility of fielding the team.

Let me propose a suggestion here that may reap dividends in many situations. It might be a good idea to extend invitations to parents of team members, or even to the membership of booster clubs interested in the athletic program. They will have an opportunity to see first-hand the initial preparation of a team for the competitive season, and provide the coach with possible assistance in two areas:

1. The parents in many cases will help encourage their sons and provide impetus to the program.
2. The fact that the members of the booster club understand what is being attempted may assist the coach in the procurement of any funds which may be required for the program.

The Agenda

Need

The establishment of need for such a conditioning program should be first on the agenda. It might help to emphasize the point if some statistics were presented relative to the overall physical condition of American youth today. The coach will usually be surprised to find that although the relatively low condition of our youngsters has been pointed up statistically, there is still wide-spread disbelief that this is true.

Parents or other adults will usually be especially hard to convince (remembering the old days), and it might be well to present statistics or results of the physical fitness test used in your particular school, including a comparison with the national norms.

Another valuable point to emphasize is the aspect of safety and injury prevention. Any coach who has been active for any period of time has observed many instances in which good physical conditioning may have prevented an injury. For instance, a high percentage of injuries in football occur toward the end of the half. You should emphasize that good conditioning and proper tonicity in the musculature can help to prevent injury in many cases.

The Facts

The pertinent facts to be presented should be chosen very carefully. You are striving for understanding, but you should not cloud the issue with unimportant trivia. Those facts presented and explained should be of such a nature that they are definitely indispensable in the operation of the program. Interest will lag if those attending the meeting are subjected to too many facts and figures not absolutely essential to basic understanding.

The following points will provide you with guidelines for a presentation encompassing most of the pertinent data which should be included.

1. *Basic Principle*

Since this is the core of the whole program, it should be established first. Remember that exposure to the "sweat complex" makes it difficult for some to understand how isometrics can be of value. Refer to Chapter Two for a reminder of this principle. Emphasize here that belief in the basic concept is necessary for effective participation.

2. *Your Contraction Time*

Be sure you distinguish between the contraction time called for in the basic principle, and the one you will utilize in the program. The importance of a brief graduation period prior to the accomplishment of a maximum contraction should be pointed out. That is, the exercise will be safer and more comfortable if a few seconds are used to attain the necessary contraction intensity. Point out, however, that the basic principle is correct in its statement that six seconds is the optimum duration of contraction.

3. *Oxygen Debt*

In order to provide the participants with a partial answer to the question "why?," it is advisable to expose them to the concept of oxygen debt.

Questions may be asked about the physiological process which takes place within the muscle after oxygen debt is incurred. At the present time, no one has the answer to this part of the question. We know that muscle fibers may be deprived of oxygen through forceful contractions, and we know that for some reason the deprivation of oxygen causes a gain in the strength level of the muscle. The process through which this occurs is still a mystery.

A reference might be made to the preceding point (number 2) regarding the fact that in order for every muscle fiber contained in the contracting muscle to experience this starvation, the contraction must be held a minimum of six seconds.

4. *Three Position Technique*

Probably the last point which needs to be presented is the concept of allowing the performer three different positions for each exercise.

Present the three position technique on the basis that development through the entire range of motion is essential, and that this procedure will help you to accomplish it.

Demonstration

The next item on the agenda is one of the most important of the entire meeting. If the exercises included in the program are performed with improper technique, the value received from participation in the conditioning program will most certainly be reduced. This fact must be made crystal-clear to the athletes!

Prior to the commencement of the initial meeting, select the exercises which are to be used in the program. As discussed in Chapter Three, inclusion of any exercise should be based upon examination of the activities performed in the sport, and the need of developing specific musculature in order to make these movements more effective. All of the time spent in selection of the program will be for naught if the exercises are not conducted in a specific manner.

1. *Emphasize the Importance of Proper Application*

Let's take an example relative to the importance of proper

technique and see why a great deal of emphasis should be placed on this point in our presentation at the meeting.

Suppose it is our intention to include an exercise to aid in the development of the quadriceps femoris. This highly important muscle group serves to extend the knee, an action that is essential in most sports. We might choose an exercise similar to a half-squat extension, which would serve our purpose admirably. In this particular exercise the coaching points state that the back should assume a position as near the vertical plane as possible. The thrust or contraction against the bar should be made *straight up*, allowing the quadriceps to be the prime movers in the action. Accomplished in the three positions noted in Chapter Seven, the exercise is excellent in development of this important muscle group.

If, on the other hand, improper positioning is assumed in the initial phase of the exercise, poor results will be realized. Suppose that instead of adhering to proper technique, a boy allows his back to assume an angle of approximately forty-five degrees in the positioning procedure. As he applies his contraction to the bar, instead of the quadriceps applying the force straight up, the musculature associated with the low back will be attempting to straighten the back to the vertical plane. Improper technique will not only reap poor results, but may prove to be detrimental, since the muscles of the lower region of the back are poorly suited for accomplishing this action against a tremendous resistance.

The process of substitution of one muscle group for another in accomplishing an action is one that must definitely be guarded against as the exercises are performed. The positioning of the performer for each exercise has been studied carefully to allow as little error as possible, and the athletes must be made aware of this fact.

2. *Use Your Team Members*

Once positioning has been established and emphasized,

the coach conducting the meeting should proceed with the demonstration. Individual preference may be exercised here with regard to who will perform the actual techniques. I find that it is a worthwhile idea to have previously coached two or three of your team members in the proper techniques for four or five exercises apiece, which they may then be called on to demonstrate. The coach can roam freely about the stage or platform, indicating specific details of each position to the audience. Choose these demonstrators carefully, as some boys have a flair for this sort of thing, while others do not.

3. *Equipment and Instructions*

Either a portable isometric device should be employed, or else a mock-up of one can be constructed with very little expense and trouble. The device should be incorporated in the presentation so that a true picture of the exercise and positions involved can be conveyed.

A mimeographed instruction sheet, distributed to the whole audience, may be used to good advantage in maintaining close attention, and provide the means of following the progress of the demonstration more closely. These instruction sheets should be retained by each member of the squad so that memories may be refreshed during actual participation in the program.

Each exercise included in the total program should be clearly demonstrated, using each of the positions necessary in accomplishing proper technique. The procedure will not occupy a great deal of time if adequate preparations are made in advance with regard to the demonstrators and the verbal material presented with the demonstration. In a normal program of ten to twelve exercises, (including specials) I would estimate that this portion might occupy about 25 minutes. You will find that it was time well spent as the program of conditioning progresses.

A word of advice. Make certain that your preparation for this phase of the presentation is more than adequate. Be sure of what you are going to say about each exercise and the need for performing it in a particular manner. Understanding may mean the difference between total or partial success to many of your squad members.

Supplemental Programs

At this point any supplemental programs to be included in conjunction with the main program should be explained and demonstrated. These would most likely fall into two categories:

1. Warm-up drills.
2. Agility drills and stretching.

It is virtually essential that some type of warm-up precede actual participation in each workout period. Every coach probably has a "pet" program of warm-up drills which are used before any practice, and various types of exercises of this nature may be employed. I would suggest that particular attention be paid to those areas of the body which will be exercised during the workout.

The following may serve as a guide in establishing the type of warm-up drill which should be used before each isometric workout:

1. Pushups – 8 to 10.
2. Situps – 8 to 10.
3. Hurdler's exercise – 4 to 5 each leg.
4. Trunk rotations (full) – 8 to 10.
5. Hamstring stretching. (Legs crossed, touching the floor outside of the foot crossed in front.) – 4 to 5 each leg.
6. Bringing the knees alternately up to the chest and "hugging" them – 4 to 5 each leg.

A program along these lines should serve to provide adequate warm-up for the exercise bout.

Agility drills and stretching types of exercises are an essential part of the total conditioning program for any sport. Their presence in the program will help insure that nothing which may increase the effectiveness of the athlete is being omitted. These drills and stretching exercises should be performed after the isometric workout, or on days when no isometrics have been scheduled.

The types of activities which are included should be along the following lines:

1. "Carioca type" leg crossing mobility drills.
2. Scramble drills.
3. Reaction drills.
4. Three point and four point wave drills.
5. Specialty drills common to each particular position in each specific sport.
6. The stretching exercises should include activities that would allow the muscles which have been contracting during the exercise program, to be lengthened. An activity as simple as a full hang for fifteen seconds from the isometric bar on a doorway will prove valuable.

Enthusiasm

Another important facet of the initial meeting is one which is non-technical, but still highly essential. The method of presentation of all of the preceding material may well serve to establish the degree of effectiveness of the entire program. Of course, being involved in the coaching profession, we all recognize the fact that the method with which *any* material is presented is extremely important. If the coach seems uninterested and unsure, his attitude is almost sure to be conveyed to the audience. On the other hand, if an air of excitement and anticipation is generated in the presentation, the audience may be expected to perceive this and very likely to be caught up in it.

The positive approach to isometrics is essential. It is more true in an activity of this nature than in many others, since in the final analysis, only the boy himself can determine how much effort he is going to put into the program. Some individuals can become very good actors as far as isometric exercises are concerned. They may appear to be straining and concentrating, while in reality they are far from approaching a maximum contraction. At VMI, a sign is hung close to the isometric racks which reads: "Psychological Intestinal Fortitude—Mental Guts. Have you got it?"

Enthusiasm generated and displayed by the coach in his presentation of isometric material to his players can mean a great deal in the attitude with which they will approach the conditioning program. Be enthusiastic!

Supervision of the Program

Once the phase of orientation has been properly completed, the problem of the supervision of the program will diminish considerably. In fact, you will be amazed to find that the program virtually runs itself. Emphasis placed on the proper introduction of isometrics to team members will prove to be extremely valuable in the specific area of supervision alone.

The author does not mean to minimize the importance of total supervision during the duration of the entire program, however. Young men are highly perceptive, and thus are quick to sense the degree of interest of the coach. To spend a great deal of effort on the initial presentation and then sit back and relax would be very unwise. The interest maintained by the participants in a program is almost a direct reflection of the interest shown by its originator. You have to convey the impression to your team that you are interested in them, and in the program, throughout its duration. If you are lax in this respect, you will soon observe the results. In athletics you have a ready-made motivational factor which should work in your favor. A boy wants to *be* on the team. If he has already accomplished this, then he wants to *stay* on the team and improve his performance. We have to make use of this factor and maintain motivation through proper supervision.

This section of the chapter will deal with methods of supervision, through which you will be able to encourage *backsliders* and those who have that common affinity towards *forgetting.*

Scheduling

One area of supervision important in the effectiveness of the program is the matter of the scheduling of workouts. Team members should not be allowed to workout indiscriminately, or at their own discretion, since they might not make the best use of the time available. What would be the most efficient schedule?

In Chapter Two, dealing with the fundamentals of isometrics, I proposed that the best schedule of workouts would probably be the alternate day method. This method is based on the fact that a sufficient amount of time (six to eight weeks) is available for conditioning prior to the beginning of the competitive season. If a lesser span of time were imposed, we would probably have to assume an everyday or five-day-per-week program. For our purposes here, let's assume that sufficient time is available to us and we can proceed with the alternate day plan. Assume that we can schedule workouts for Monday, Wednesday, and Friday. This means we have at least two days of the week for advancement of our supplemental program. We can utilize these days in any manner we see fit, either by establishing an isotonic program, or employing them for our agility and specialty drills. Let's say we decide to include the latter. On Mondays, Wednesdays, and Fridays our team engages in isometrics, and on Tuesdays and Thursdays they work on agility and specialty drills. This leaves Saturday and Sunday as our rest or "growth" period. This particular program is excellent for a six to eight week type.

1. *Team Scheduling*

If there is an entire block of time available to the team as a whole, no problem exists. With proper organization, a large number of boys may be run through a typical program in a short time. Equipment used in isometrics may be constructed so cheaply and quickly that there should be no problem in making enough devices available to the whole team. If the coach wants to utilize the standard "bar type" of device, two or three men can exercise at the same time on a single bar. Also, a common director could oversee the whole program, telling the men which exercise and position to use, and timing the contraction for all of the racks as a whole. As soon as one group completes their required contraction time, a new group quickly takes their places and the bar remains in the same position for that same phase of the exercise. A short lapse of time between contractions will not appreciably diminish the effects of the exercise.

Using mass methods such as these, the whole squad could work out on the same day in the span of thirty minutes or so.

2. *Individual Scheduling*

Now to the problem of scheduling individuals. If the whole team cannot work out simultaneously, then the coach should secure a *free time* schedule from each of the squad members. These schedules should include those portions of the day when it is possible for that person to have his workout.

A space of twenty minutes is sufficient in most cases. Next, construct a master schedule so that you know when each individual on your team is exercising, insuring you of the fact that each man is adhering to the time table. The athletes should be advised that any deviation from the master schedule is to be reported to the coach so that if need be, modifications can be instituted.

Buddy System

If it is necessary to resort to a schedule in which team members are exercising at different hours, (and even possibly on different days) then it may be a good idea to use a buddy system during exercise bouts. Normally in most high school or college situations there is rarely a time when only one person has the opportunity of working isometrically. If possible, at least two people should share a workout period. This is desirable for a number of reasons:

1. In any exercises involving a supine or prone position, the bar can be changed to the new positions by the performer's buddy, without the necessity of the performer getting out of position.
2. The buddy can time the contraction of the performer. Since there is a tendency to begin to speed up the count as a person tires, this can be very valuable.
3. The buddy is in a position whereby he can check the technique of the performer. In many exercises, it is extremely easy to vary from the desired position without realizing it. The person observing the performer can help correct any discrepancies he notices in positioning and technique.
4. Exercising alone is usually undesirable from a motivational standpoint. Therefore, if possible, athletes should not be permitted to exercise by themselves.

Charts

The use of an easily read and checked chart should be included in the supervision of a program. The chart should definitely include the following information:

1. Name
2. Weight (before workout)
3. A system for checking the date of performance.
4. A list of exercises to be performed.

A portion of a chart such as this appears below:

AME	WEIGHT			2 ARM CURL			UPRIGHT ROWING		
	M	W	F						
1st Week				X	X	X			
2nd Week									
3rd Week									
4th Week									
5th Week									
6th Week									
7th Week									
8th Week									

As may be seen, the chart would indicate to the observer that weight had been noted on Monday, Wednesday, and Friday, and all required exercises had been performed on a specific day.

If a coach preferred to grant some latitude to the performer in regard to specific exercises to be engaged in during a single workout, then the boy would check only those exercises actually performed.

Delegation of Authority

It is my contention that a coach should delegate some of the responsibility of supervision to his staff, while still maintaining his direct contact with the program.

One of the best methods of sharing this duty is to include the student managers and trainers. On the one hand, they will feel more an integral part of the team, and on the other, you will have ready-made checkers and overseers once they are properly oriented and know what you expect from them. These trainers and managers can construct all of the charts and attendance checking methods which are to be used, and maintain the same throughout the program. It has been my experience that personnel such as these boys will enter into a program whole-heartedly, even to the point of participating along with the team members. The right type of individuals in the position of managers and trainers can be a fertile source of assistance in an isometrics program.

The coach will also probably want to include the assistant coaches so that each man on the staff will have a working knowledge of the total program. If an alternate day method of conditioning is used, coaches can be made responsible for checking on the performance of the team on a single day per week.

Keep in mind however, that the final responsibility for

the maintenance of a high level of interest and response falls on the shoulders of the head coach.

SUMMARY

The areas of orientation and supervision cannot be neglected in the total scheme of a conditioning program if maximum results are to be achieved.

Orientation is the first consideration of the coach when instituting a new program of isometrics, and one of the major concerns should be that of an initial meeting. The meeting should be based on an agenda similar to the following:

I. *Team Meeting.*
- A. *The need for the program.*
    1. National statistics.
    2. Particular statistics.
- B. *The facts.*
    1. Basic principle.
    2. Contraction time.
    3. Oxygen debt.
    4. Three position technique.
- C. *Demonstrations.*
    1. Importance of proper technique.
    2. Review all exercises.
    3. Make a mimeographed copy available to all.
- D. *Supplemental Programs.*
    1. Warm-up prior to exercise.
    2. Demonstration of stretching and agility exercises.
- E. *Enthusiasm.*
    1. Presentation of material in an enthusiastic manner.
    2. Foster enthusiasm in the participants.

After the initial phase of orientation has been completed, it remains for the coach to oversee and supervise the total program so that high interest and motivation may be maintained.

The coach should utilize all of his available personnel in this process, while still remaining the prime mover behind the whole program.

CHAPTER FIVE

Effective Testing: The Key to Success

All of the preceding chapters deal with material essential in the establishment and accomplishment of an effective conditioning program. Care must be taken by the administrator to afford each of these essentials the attention they deserve.

On the other hand, if we were required to rate these essentials in the order of their total contribution to a program, the area of evaluation would have to occupy first position. On no other area does the success or failure of a conditioning program depend to such a degree. Let's look at some of the reasons for its importance.

Importance of Motivation

The concept of motivation has been touched upon briefly in the preceding chapters. The fact remains that the importance of this area is so great that it is virtually impossible to overemphasize it.

Boys and young men are competitive by nature. If they were not, then we as coaches would not be likely to come into contact with them in a professional capacity. Nurture this attribute of competitiveness in an athlete, and you have a potential winner. Suppress it, and you are left with an indifferent participant, going along for the ride. As coaches, we are so highly concerned with the area of morale and spirit, that we devise all types of methods to foster it. The stars on the helmet for interceptions, the vari-colored helmets to denote one hundred-percenters, etc. All of these gimmicks aid us in creating and maintaining the air of competition. I support all of these attempts, and would carry them even further, to the point of instilling competitive attitude in our squads even before the season begins. How can this be done?

Making Your Program Competitive

Let's be frank. Suppose that we have been using only the isotonic form of training in our conditioning program. Athlete A is 6′0 and weighs 200 pounds. Athlete B is exactly the same weight and height. Let's assume that the entire team was given a sort of strength test before the conditioning program began, consisting of something even as simple as a bench press for maximum. Athlete A accomplished a 250 pound press, athlete B only 210 pounds. The former would then assume that at that point he was stronger than the latter. On a succeeding test, A manages 260 pounds, and B presses 240 pounds. Now both boys are allowed to achieve a sense of satisfaction. A, because he is still stronger than his counterpart, B because his rate of increase is higher than A's. Both boys are motivated, and exhibit interest in the conditioning program.

Assume now that we incorporate isometrics in the program. The entire picture changes. Now both boys are working side by side on duplicate racks, and they both note that regardless of the pressure applied to the bars, there is really no indication of who is contracting more forcefully. Now we are faced with the situation in which the boys may continue their participation in the program simply on the impetus provided by the exhortations of the coach, but not through any real sense of accomplishment or pride. Why not use the same test we used when we were training with isotonics? I feel that this method (lifting for maximum) should be used only with an isotonic program, since it is so closely allied with the actual training procedures used. A testing program is much more valuable if the method of testing simulates the techniques used in conditioning. If this concept is accepted, then we need a program of evaluation utilizing a system closely approximating isometric techniques. How this may be achieved will be discussed shortly.

Benefits for the Coach

We should all be agreed that an evaluation system is imperative from the standpoint of the athletes. What value does it have from the viewpoint of the coach? First, we should be as interested as the boys are in the various strength levels of our athletes. Possession of this knowledge might aid us in making some of our decisions regarding personnel. More important, an evaluation program has the additional benefit of allowing the coach to observe the concrete effects of his program, or in some cases, the lack of effect. Observation is a handy tool in rating the results of a program already in use, permitting the coach to make those changes or adjustments which may be necessary in order to accomplish the desired results. For example, based on test results, it may be indicated that more time should be allowed for work on the legs, or that too many exercises are included for one portion of the body and not enough for another. An evaluation program can be a valuable asset for a coach, and one which should be effectively utilized to its greatest extent.

Selecting the Method That Is Right for You

Let's assume that we are all in agreement concerning the fact that in order to achieve a high degree of interest in an isometric program, an evaluation procedure must be included in the total picture. Your next concern is selecting a method which can be employed to the best advantage in our particular situations. Here are some items which should be considered in the selection of such a method.

Expense

The matter of the cost of testing equipment will definitely have to be a consideration in most coaching situations. In most cases, you are constantly fighting the battle of the budget in order to procure those items which are absolutely essential for your teams . . . uniforms, equipment, etc., with the result that very little money is available for anything that is not essential for simply fielding the team. This indicates that any method chosen should be inexpensive enough to allow you to purchase the necessary equipment without causing an undue strain on your budget. Certainly, some excellent devices for evaluation are available to those who are able to afford sums in the hundreds of dollars for their procurement. Brochures are supplied from many sources relative to their availability, and most of you are familiar with them. The value of these expensive devices is unquestioned in relation to research projects and in experimentation, but the fact is that the vast majority of coaches could not possibly obtain them without a capital expenditure out of proportion to their entire budgets.

For our purposes, let us omit the discussion of the merits of any device, the price of which might exceed the sum of approximately $50.00. In many cases, the total cost of the testing device will not even approach this figure. Now that we have decided to confine our search of methods to those which are well within the reach of most coaches, let's continue with our discussion of the qualifications that any of these methods must possess in order to best fulfill our needs.

Providing a Number

Let's establish the fact right now that you are not primarily interested in pure scientific research. At some time later on in the program you may wish to delve into this area, employing rigid testing conditions, control groups, etc. These projects are certainly interesting and worthwhile, but in the final analysis, the coach is simply interested in determining how strong one boy is in relation to a norm, or how much progress has been made in attaining strength through the use of the conditioning program.

In order to achieve your purpose, a method must be used which will be standardized as far as the results of the initial and successive tests are concerned. What is meant here is that in order for you to be provided with some method of observing results, an object must be moved over a calibrated distance, a dial must swing to a number, or an indicator must rise to a certain height. For your purposes, it is not necessary that a test be calibrated in tensile-pounds or horsepower or any other established measurement. The indication of a number by a dial, or the difference in a linear measurement will suffice in indicating gain or less.

Once a norm or average has been determined, through an initial test, results can be charted according to this number, rather than in relation to any specific established indication such as pounds or horsepower.

Any method we select then, should provide us with some type of number so that succeeding tests may be compared in order to determine progression or regression.

Portability

The method we select should not involve cumbersome material that cannot be stored away. In most coaching situations, (especially in high school) space is at a premium. In some cases coaches are hard-pressed to find an area in which the boys may exercise. Available space, once it has been secured, should be used for the purpose for which it is intended, namely exercising, without having to allot some of it for bulky equipment. If the equipment to be used is portable, it can be stored in any area available for it, without inconveniencing anyone.

An added benefit of portability is that the device may be transported easily to areas in which clinics or assemblies are to be presented, making the device available for inclusion in the program.

Accessibility of Materials

Since we will consider appliances which may be homemade later on in this chapter, one of your considerations should be that of the availability of materials necessary for their construction. These devices require very little welding, threading and the like. The raw materials necessary in making the device are available in local stores in most cities, or able to be supplied through most catalogue companies.

If we are to keep the cost of our particular device down to a minimum, then accessibility of materials must be considered.

Easily Constructed

Although in our profession it is often necessary for us to assume many different responsibilities, I don't feel that we should be required to be carpenters or plumbers in order to construct a suitable device for testing. None of the suggestions dealt with later on in the chapter require an engineering degree for their construction, allowing the coach and/or his managers to complete the job with a minimum of scraped knuckles and expended elbow grease.

If any problems arise in the process of construction, it may behoove the coach to enlist the aid of the school's manual training department. It has been my experience that in most cases, school shops welcome the opportunity of engaging in worthwhile projects that may be of value to the school.

The device we select, therefore, should definitely be easy to construct, should it be necessary to do so.

Easily Administered

The method of evaluation should be simple enough to be administered with a minimum of preparation and personnel. It should be such that one, or possibly two men can set up, administer and record the test results in one session. If the evaluation method requires an involved administrative procedure, the interest of the persons being tested will be diminished to the point where a maximum effort will not be obtained.

In my opinion, any test method which incorporates the

six criteria discussed previously will prove to be a valuable evaluation procedure.

Use of Existing Tests

Before we wander too far afield in our discussion of usable tests, let's consider for a moment the possibility of incorporating well-known fitness test items into the evaluation scheme. This provides a fertile area from which the coach may draw, since most of these tests are not only familiar to young athletes, but in many cases norms of performances have been established providing the coach with a ready-made yardstick to use in measuring his particular groups.

Once we begin to consider this area, probably a number of tests will occur to each individual coach. Consider all the possibilities and incorporate those which adhere to most of the six principles previously outlined. If a test item possesses most of these qualities it may be used effectively in your testing program.

To illustrate the type of test which may prove to be valuable to you, let me suggest a few of the many possibilities in the area of existing tests.

Vertical Jump Test

The vertical jump test helps to indicate the improvement of the strength level in the lower extremities. True, the action is explosive in nature, whereas the training has been isometric, but it still provides an excellent indication.

The test equipment may be easily constructed by the school shop, or by the coach himself. A board, constructed of wood, plastic or slate may be used. The board should be cut and marked off along the lines of the one represented in Fig. 1. (In some cases, if it is more convenient, the markings may be placed directly on a wall.)

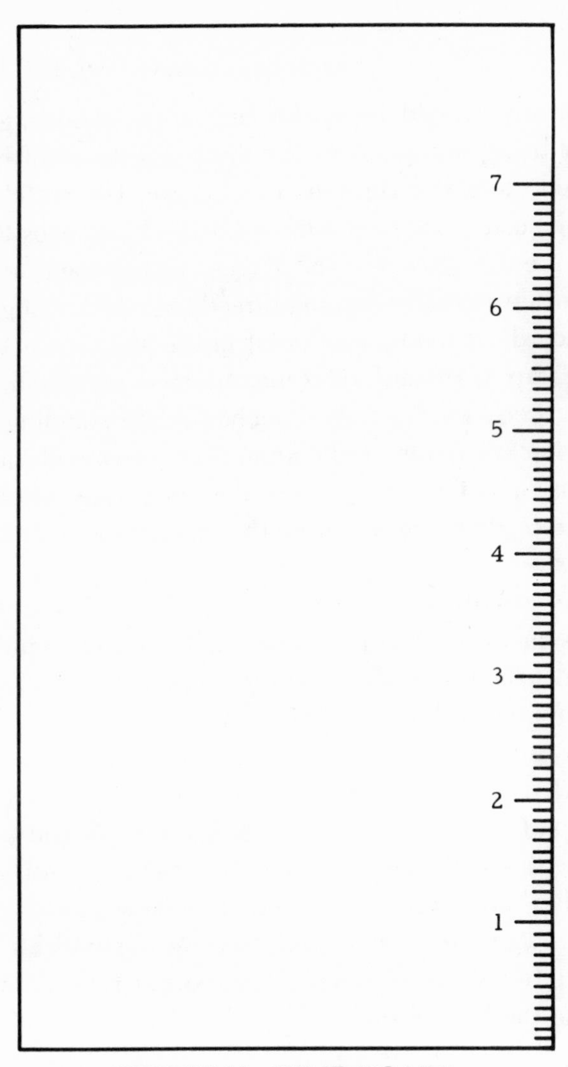

VERTICAL JUMP BOARD

FIG. 1

Attach the board to a wall at a height which permits the shortest boy to be tested to reach the lower portion of it while standing flat-footed, and not so low that the tallest man may be able to reach off the scale when he jumps. Some adjustment may be necessary in this respect.

The test should be conducted in the following manner. The boy being tested covers the fingers of the right hand with powdered chalk or magnesium carbonate. He stretched up as high as he can while remaining flat-footed, and taps the board. If need be, he re-covers the fingers of the hand with chalk and then sets himself to spring directly upward, along the path of the board. At the highest point in the jump, he is instructed to again tap the board. The measurement in this test should be made between the point touched while standing, and the mark made at the top of the jump. This mark will indicate his true jumping ability. If at all possible, two trials should be permitted, recording the better of the two jumps.

Medicine Ball Push

The medicine ball push may be employed to indicate the strength of the extensors of the arms and shoulders. Fig. 2 illustrates how the test area should look.

The subject should be seated, with the legs extended and spread. This posture helps minimize the effects of the throw on any parts of the body other than the torso and arms. The ball is held with a basketball type grip and permitted to drop to the "lap" area prior to the actual pushing motion. The athlete attempts to achieve as much distance as possible with the throw. Here again, it is advisable to permit two or three trials, recording the best of the group.

FIG. 2

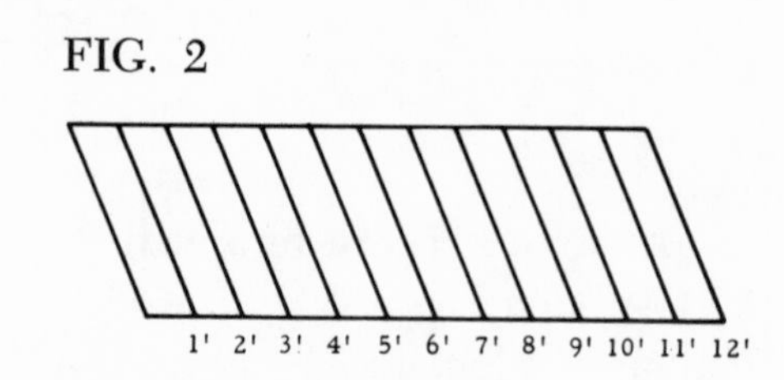

MEDICINE BALL PUT

Person being tested should have both heels behind the restraining line. Legs should remain extended throughout the trials.

Calibrated area may begin a short distance from the subject, so that measurement and marking of lines may be kept to a minimum.

Pullups

Pullups tend to indicate the strength level present in the flexors of the arms and the shoulder depressors. Extreme care must be taken in the administration of this test, however, since it has been my experience that, in many cases, a lack of standardization of technique has produced spurious indications. Use the same technique on the initial tests and all succeeding ones to insure reliable indications. Do not allow a swinging motion or "kipping" up to the bar. Make certain that the chin is completely over the bar on each pullup. Count any near-completion toward the close of the test as a half, and not whole accomplishment. For varieties sake, the pullup test may be performed with a forward grip or reverse grip on the bar. Separate sets of data should be recorded for these different types of grips.

These few possibilities which have been mentioned are certainly only a small number of the many fitness items which might possibly be used in an evaluation program. The author discusses them only to indicate a few of the many exercises available in this type of evaluative procedure. The individual coach can make his own selections for testing, and may even wish to include one or two exercises that inject a "fun" atmosphere into the testing program. Athletes are most familiar with these tests, having been exposed to them in most cases since elementary school, and as a result they usually have a deep sense of satisfaction when they show up well. I would certainly not recommend that all of the test procedures used be of this type, but they may certainly be utilized to provide a "change of pace."

Inexpensive Mechanical Devices

It is the contention of the author that any evaluation program should include at least one, or a combination of inexpensive mechanical devices. As stated previously, when we propose "inexpensive" equipment, we are excluding those particular devices costing over fifty dollars. The cost of equipment discussed here is relatively low, enabling the coach or staff to procure it in some manner, even if the actual team budget prohibits it. I have found that in many high schools, varsity letter clubs, booster clubs, and related organizations may be approached relative to obtaining the equipment and usually they are only too happy to comply, when they realize that they will be aiding the team in a concrete way.

There are a number of these devices available on the market, and we will discuss a few of them in order to illustraate their value to the evaluation program.

Grip Manuometer

The grip manuometer is somewhat limited as to the type of musculature it can measure, but the cost of one is so low that it may be included as a specialized type of device. The purchase price is well below the fifty dollar limit we imposed, and they are available from many sources, including the Gymnastic Supply Company. A diagram of one of these manuometers appears in Fig. 3.

The device should be placed *dial side down* into the palm of the hand. This prevents the thumb or fingers of the person being tested from interfering with the movement of the indicator. As the athlete squeezes the device, he should be cautioned against putting his elbow near the body so as to prevent

FIG. 3

any leverage from occurring. The manuometer has a dial which remains at the point of peak effort, so the athlete should simply hand the manuometer back to the tester for recording. The test should be conducted with both hands, recording each set of data. An interesting sidelight may be observed as the testing program continues. At first, there will be a significant difference in scores produced by the dominant and non-dominant hands. As the exercise program progresses a few weeks, the difference or gap will begin to diminish in most cases, since both hands must be used equally in most of the exercise techniques.

The manuometer is restricted to testing grip strength alone in its original shape, but with some ingenuity and thought it may be modified to test other areas of the body. For example, one might press it while it was held in place on a table, or squeeze it between the wrists, securing some further data for the records. Even if it is used strictly for the purpose intended, it is an excellent method of determining the amount of grip strength present in an individual.

Push-Pull Dynamometer

Here again, there are a number of different models available. Some of these may require a sum over the limit that has been imposed, so we will discuss one type which is within the confines of our budget. A model is shown in Fig. 4.

FIG. 4

The interesting advantage of the illustrated dynamometer over other models is the fact that the principal component is actually a grip manuometer which may be detached. The handles and vise-like components are available from the same company which manufactures the manuometer (The Gymnastic Supply Company).

When the device is rigged in this manner, its uses are increased considerably. Now the equipment is able to record varying types of actions. Lifting, compression, expansion, and depression may all be measured with this device. Here again the ingenuity of the coach is the only factor which determines exactly how many uses may be possible. If desired, one part of the device may be stabilized or held in a fixed position in order to establish data for particular exercises or movements.

The dynamometer, with modifications, may be used to test not only the arms, shoulders, back and other areas of the torso, but the legs as well. It can prove to be a valuable, inexpensive addition to your testing program.

Iso-Scale

Designed to be used in conjunction with an Iso-kit, the Iso-Scale is available from Coaches Sporting Goods Company, of Marion, Indiana. A model of the Iso-Scale is shown in Fig. 5.

The Iso-Scale is valuable in that it has an ability to be used in a number of various positions. Modifications and adjustments are very simple and can be accomplished quickly. It is attached to an iso-kit by threading the loops of the strap through the bars on the top and bottom of the scale. Because it may be moved to any position along the entire length of the strap, it may be rapidly adjusted to accommodate variances in body build.

A further advantage of this device is the fact that by substituting the bar on the isometric rack for the one normally used with the Iso-kit an athlete is able to actually exercise

FIG. 5

with the implement, noting his maximum contraction in each of the positions used. This is possible because another feature of the scale, the memory dial, will stay at the maximum position until re-set, enabling the performer to read it at his ease. The memory dial is also valuable from the testing standpoint, since the recorder or coach can devote his attention to the technique being used, rather than having to rivet his eyes on a scale or dial.

The Iso-Scale may be used to test the strength of the athlete in virtually all of the positions used in a normal exercise program. The scale is simply attached to the strap and the athlete performs the exercise desired, enabling the recorder to secure his maximum in any position for which the bar is set. An extremely useful device for evaluation, the Iso-Scale is well within the price range we have established.

As I mentioned previously, there are a number of inexpensive mechanical devices available to us for use in our evaluation programs. The three which have been discussed are indicative of this type of apparatus. It would be wise for the coach to look through the professional brochures and catalogs available to him before selecting a particular device so that he will be assured that the model will fulfill his needs most satisfactorily.

Simple, Home-Made Devices

Here is an area in which the mind of the coach with imagination and ingenuity can excell. In this section we are going to discuss methods of constructing evaluation devices utilizing raw materials which are readily available to everyone, at very little cost. These methods or devices, employed correctly and with some thought, can be every bit as reliable and functional as many commercial ones. There is no end to the number of ways in which household and other common materials can serve us in our quest for test data. The devices which will be mentioned are only a few of the myriad number of possibilities, and no coach or reader should feel bound to incorporate only those ideas set forth here. Let your imagination run free, and you will find that one of the major considerations of an evaluation program . . . cost, will play a more and more diminished role in our thinking.

All of the devices discussed will adhere to the six principles previously advanced governing the selection of an adequate, reliable testing program.

Home-Made Grip Strength Indicator

Through the use of a couple of simple, available ingredients, a functional grip strength indicator may be constructed. The materials necessary are: a squeeze-type plastic bottle (such as the type used in laboratories or the mustard and catsup containers used in commercial establishments), a rubber stopper with a hole in it, a glass tube closed at one end, colored water, and a yardstick. The apparatus is assembled as indicated in Fig. 6.

As the athlete squeezes the plastic bottle, it will cause the colored water in the container to be forced up through the glass tube. The greater the pressure, the higher the column of colored fluid will rise. The height of the column may be recorded by observing the yardstick located behind the tube. If any adjustments are required, that is if the height of the column is too high or low for practical purposes, it may be controlled by increasing the size of the plastic container, the firmness of it, or the diameter of the glass tubing used.

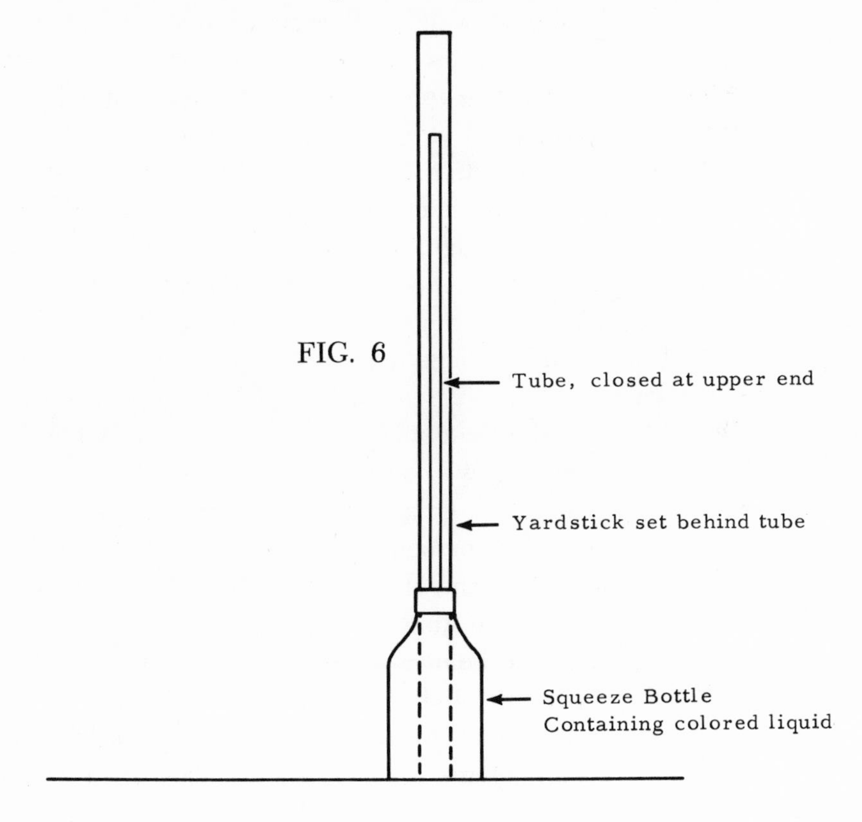

FIG. 6

This effective device can be made as a laboratory assignment in the school chemistry or physics lab, providing the coach with a number of such indicators.

As with the manuometer, tests should be conducted with both hands.

Spring Scale Device

The use of a simple spring scale will prove to be very valuable in our strength testing program. These scales are available at local hardware stores, and come in a variety of sizes and capacities. Since the cost of a single unit is so low, a number may be purchased with relatively little outlay.

Of course, many different types of pulls and pushes are possible through the use of a single, unadorned unit, but because we are striving for reliability and feasibility, I suggest a device constructed along the lines of the one indicated in Fig. 7. Upon inspection, alternate methods of assembly may be apparent to those among you who possess an affinity for construction and design, and any modifications which might serve to increase its effectiveness should in no way be discouraged. Remember, ingenuity is the key concept in this area.

The assembly diagramed in Fig. 7 has a number of advantages.

1. Since the limits of most of these scales is below two hundred pounds, if we construct them in parallel, we reduce the reading indicated on a single unit, allowing us to test even the more powerful anatomical areas (such as the legs).

2. The use of the chains allows for adjustment to body size and exercise or testing position. In order to make sure that the same links are being used on both sides, I have found it helpful to count the links from one end and paint or attach a marker to every fifth one. This also aids in quick attachment.

3. The arrangement of the sectionalized lower assembly

requires the athlete to exert the force on the bar bilaterally, rather than with a dominant arm or leg.

4. The base board may be attached directly to the floor, so that the athlete will not be required to stand on it for anchoring purposes. This also allows a bench or table to be placed in position so that any supine, prone or sitting movement may be measured.

5. The device allows the coach to test almost any movement or exercise position desired, since the modifications made possible by the use of the chains permits pulling, lifting, side raising, and most extension maneuvers to be tested.

The readings on the scales should be made by a recorder seated directly in front of them. It is only necessary to ob-

FIG. 7

SPRING SCALE DEVICE

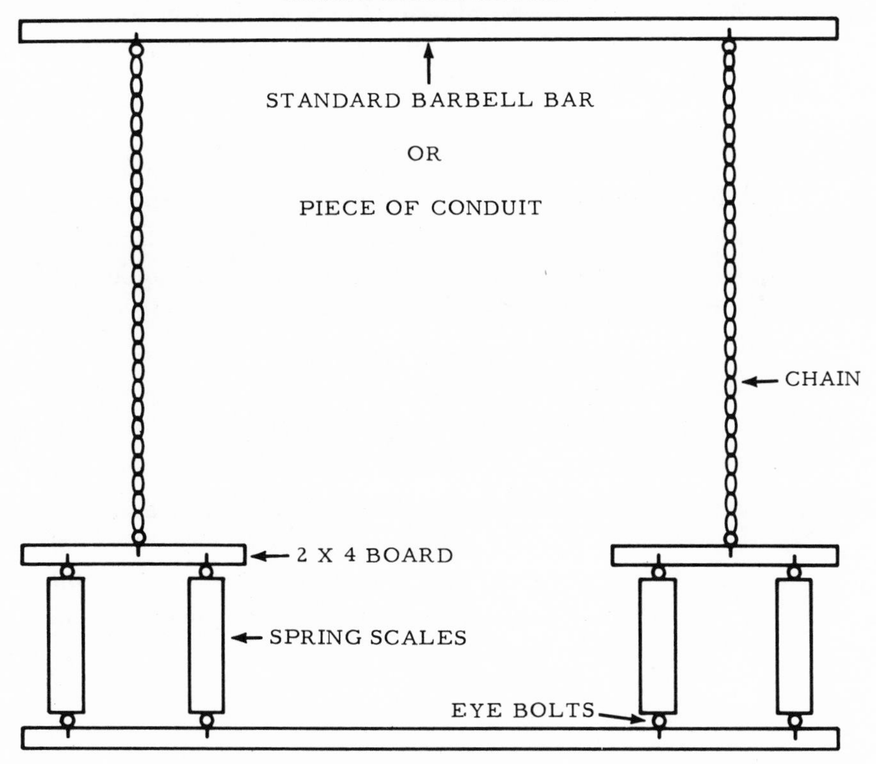

serve one of the scales, since the force is disseminated to all of them equally. It is also advisable to read the same scale at all times so that any variance factor is reduced.

The entire cost of the device may vary slightly, but with some help from the school shop, it can usually be assembled for under fifteen dollars. In view of the low cost, the coach can utilize two or three of them in order to speed the testing procedure, or assemble specialized units.

Bathroom Scale Device

Progressing further into the area of homemade devices, we find another excellent component for use in our evaluation procedure. Again, the article is readily available in department or hardware stores, usually at a price of less than five dollars per unit. The only considerations in our choice of the scale should be its durable construction and an easy to read dial. The limit of most commercial bathroom scales is three hundred pounds, so I suggest that you employ our parallel construction principle once more.

The Performer Provides the Movement

After experimentation with varying the position of the scale used in order to accommodate the different maneuvers required in a total testing program, we decided to let the scales remain in a fixed position, and force the performer to provide the movement. This principle also permits you to construct a very simple type of arrangement with no moving parts. Actually all that is required in the way of basic materials is an isometric device, (a rack is used in the illustration) two bathroom scales and a few pieces of lumber. Fig. 8 indicates the manner in which the materials should be assembled.

Again, if the device can be made more effective or better suited to a particular situation, then changes should by all means be made. Fig. 8 is simply a suggestion for construction. Some advantages that this method has are:

1. The baseboard or crib which contains the scales may be constructed to be portable or fixed directly to the floor.

2. The board on which the athlete stands is prevented from slipping by the box-like construction of the crib.

3. The athlete is not hampered in performing any type of contraction on the device.

4. If movements involving the prone, supine, or sitting position are to be used, two legs of the bench or table may be placed on the board, and the movement performed.

5. If any adjustment is necessary regarding the reading obtained (too high) then a third scale may be inserted under the middle of the board, reducing the resultant indications to a more feasible level.

FIG. 8

Crib for bathroom scales designed for use under isometric rack.

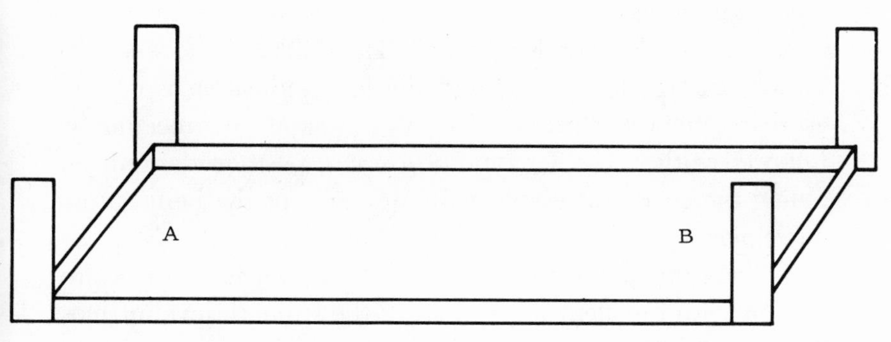

Length --- 4 feet

Width --- Determined by the size of the scales used. They should fit snugly into the crib.

Height of front, back and sides -- 2"
Height of corner posts -- 12"

Scales should be placed at points A and B, with the board (2 X 6) on which the subject will stand extending through the corner posts.

6. An isometric device actually used in training or exercising is utilized so that purchase of additional equipment is not necessary.

7. If a device other than an isometric rack is to be used, the rope, strap or chain may be looped directly under the scale. I prefer the incorporation of the rack, however.

8. The device may be used even during the regular exercise bout, enabling the performer to observe an indication of his maximum contraction as he works.

Testing Procedure

The procedure used in testing is very simple. Suppose that you wished to test the maximum of an individual's military press. The bar is set at the desired position in the isometric rack. The athlete then steps onto the board and adjusts himself in position. At this point, the recorder or coach makes a note of the reading on one of the scales. The reading indicates the weight of the board and the body weight of the athlete in all cases. The athlete then performs the pressing movement, and a maximum indication is recorded. The difference between the initial reading of the scale and the final indication is entered as that athlete's effort on that trial. The same procedure is followed with any other type of exercise position desired, enabling the coach to test virtually any area of the body in any movement chosen.

The principle of the device is simple, but its use can provide us with excellent indications of the strength level of most body areas. Again I exhort the reader to change, modify or improve on the effectiveness of any of these suggested devices, so that greater reliability or ease of administration will result.

Tips on Testing

The following section deals with random ideas and principles that should be used in the testing program in order to achieve the best possible results. All of these items should prove to be applicable in most situations, since I feel they are inherent in any intelligent testing program. The incorporation of some or all of these suggestions could possibly mean the difference between an ineffective program and one which will be valuable and interesting.

Testing Periods

After selecting a testing program and assembling the necessary equipment, it is important to use good administrative judgment. The basic principle involved here is not to let your testing program interfere with the conditioning regimen. If a great deal of the time is spent in testing, little time will be available for the necessary conditioning workouts. The interval between test periods should be such that enough time will have elapsed between the previous test and the present one so that the individuals involved will have made enough progress to be significant. If tests were conducted every other day, the gains in strength might be so small that the athletes would become discouraged and their interest would lag. The test periods should be spaced so that the squad looks forward to them as a challenge to be met.

For these reasons, I feel it is advisable to limit the test periods to once a week at the maximum, and even more ideally, every ten or twelve days. This lapse would allow for the increase to be significant, and would also provide enough sets of data to be obtained so that they could be meaningfully charted.

Indicating Results

In order for the interest of the squad to remain high, the

results of the testing program should be indicated. This will enable the athletes who are scoring well to achieve a sense of satisfaction and push them toward greater efforts, and may also provide a means of motivating those who are not progressing because of poor workout habits or laziness. How should the results be indicated?

In most situations, the results of tests are simply indicated by writing in the numerical scores of the squad on a roster-type list, and these figures require a great deal of inspection in order to glean information from them.

I suggest that the test results be put on individual graphs. Each man on the squad should have his own graph sheet posted, with the various test items indicated by a standardized key or legend. Admittedly, the numerical value of different graphs will not be the same, but each boy's initial test is the indicator as to how the step-intervals should be plotted. If this system is used, then a cursory inspection of the graphs will indicate to both the boy and the coach that he is possibly gaining in some areas and progressing more slowly in others. This would tend to indicate that he was stronger in these areas at the start of the program, or that more emphasis is needed in these areas in the conditioning program.

An additional "gimmick" which might be used to advantage is the formation of clubs or teams relative to the results of testing. For instance, it might provide additional motivation and increased interest to list the ten strongest men on the squad in each of the test items. Boys are always interested in who is the strongest among them. Then too, so that smaller boys on the squad could have something to strive for, an additional list could be posted, containing the names of those boys who achieved the greatest advance in each of the test items over their former scores. By using both of these methods, each man on the squad is provided with a goal, allowing him to compete not only against himself, but others. Both of these methods have proven to be effective in my experience.

Testing Techniques

There are a few very important concepts that should be included in this area. Their importance lies in the fact that improper technique used in the test trials may easily produce counterfeit results.

Area Testing

The coach should select exercises or test positions encompassing all of the areas of the body essential for effective performance in the particular sport. This does not mean that ten testing positions are indicated, but that at least one test position should be included for the major musculature in a particular area. A selective type of testing provides you with a meaningful indication as to the over-all condition of the musculature.

Positioning

The aspect of standardized body positioning for each individual test trial is extremely important. The strength of a muscle varies to a degree throughout its range of motion. Suppose that we are attempting to obtain test results on the flexors of the arm, and choose the two-arm curl as our test technique. If the first man who tests is six feet two and the bar is adjusted so that his elbows are flexed to about ninety degrees, and the next man to be tested is only five feet nine, then we *must* make an adjustment in the height of the bar so that his elbows are flexed to ninety degrees too! Otherwise, one of the men would have an advantage over the other as far as leverage is concerned. The bar must be adjusted properly to accommodate all of those tested, or else erroneous indications will result.

Technique

Each man to be tested must perform the test technique in exactly the same manner. Here again we will not achieve ideal results if we do not adhere to the principle. If we are testing the two-arm curl, then each man must receive the same instructions . . . keep the elbows out of the hips, do not rise on the toes, do not lean back, and pull with a steady, sustained effort rather than with a jerky type of movement.

Test Personnel

For the reasons suggested in point three above, it is my suggestion that two people be used in administering any tests. The coach or someone who understands exactly what is required should have the responsibility of constant observation of the person being tested, while another individual should be occupied with observing the scale or dial and recording the results. If any variation in technique is observed by the coach, the individual should be ordered to cease that particular trial immediately, rest, then re-assume the test position and repeat the trial. It may take a little more time to administer the tests during the initial session, but strict adherence to this concept will pay large dividends in accurate results.

Isolation of Musculature

Isolation of musculature is extremely important in scientific research and in the environment of experimentation. If we are interested in exactly how much a particular individual muscle group has gained in strength, we would have to take elaborate precautions to preclude the use of any muscular compensation.

In our case however, I don't feel that it is necessary to refine the testing procedure to this degree. In athletic activities, our main concern is with gross muscle movement, and as such, an indication of pulling or pushing power is just as valuable as far as indicative results are concerned, as are the test results on an isolated muscle group. For example, we are concerned with the strength of the entire flexion movement of the arms, rather than in the degree of improvement in the biceps brachii or the anterior deltoid alone.

Let me repeat that muscular isolation *is* important in research work, but has a lesser importance in the results for which we are striving.

SUMMARY

The concept of evaluation in any conditioning program is paramount in the achievement of an intelligent and interesting program.

Motivation of the participants can spell the success or failure of your training program, and a well-designed testing procedure is the means by which motivation may be stimulated and maintained.

One additional thought in conclusion. The coach's role relative to this whole idea is an important and necessary one. Enthusiasm is contagious, and if the coach maintains a genuine interest in the progress of the squad . . . not only initially, but a continuing one . . . then the boys cannot help but be swept along on a wave of concern. As with any new concept which may be presented by the coach to a squad, let them know that you believe in it and are truly concerned with the results, and the interest and motivation will remain high, providing its own impetus to the conditioning and evaluation programs.

CHAPTER SIX

The Upper Extremities

If the statement were made to the effect that the arms, hands, and wrists played an important role in all aspects of athletics, the reaction of the reader would more than likely be one of great surprise. "What's he telling us that for?" "Anyone knows that!"

Yes, this is true. On the other hand, how many coaches have ever stopped to consider exactly *how* important this area of the body is to an athlete? Considering not only those gross movements and actions apparent even to the spectators sitting in the stands, but some of the more finite movements as well, we come to the realization that development of strength in this area is a paramount necessity . . . not a luxury.

By way of illustration, let's consider three sports and enumerate some of those types of movements which cannot be *effectively* accomplished without a high level of development in the arms, hands, and wrists.

Football

1. Passing, by the quarterbacks and halfbacks
2. Snapping, both "T" and the long snap by the centers
3. Tackling, by all ball players
4. Catching the football, by all receivers
5. Forearm lift, by linemen
6. Hand shiver, by linemen
7. Support during scramble blocks, by linemen
8. Option pitch, by quarterbacks
9. Straight-arm, by ball carriers
10. Securing the football, by ball carriers
11. Quarterback mechanics (fakes, hand-offs, etc.)
12. Arm blocking punts or passes by defensive linemen
13. Hand-fighting for the ball when it is "up for grabs", by defensive backs
14. Supporting the body weight when diving or rolling to avoid contact or a pile-up

Basketball

1. Shooting

   a. Hook
   b. Jump
   c. Push
   d. Set
   e. Lay-up
2. Passing
   a. Bounce
   b. Chest
   c. Hook
   d. Baseball
   e. Underhand
3. Securing the ball on rebounds
4. Tap-in shots while rebounding
5. Controlling a tip-off
6. Dribbling
7. Defensive "takes" against shots
8. Receiving the ball
9. Controlling the ball in tie-up situations
10. Keeping the hands up throughout the game on defense

Baseball

1. Throwing
2. Hitting
3. Tagging a base-runner
4. Fielding the ball

Admittedly, by comparison the list for baseball appears abbreviated. However, except for the omission of running, the list contains all of the essentials of a good baseball player.

After scanning the preceding lists, the fact becomes readily apparent that development of the upper appendages is a prime requisite.

The exercises included here are designed to accomplish this task.

EXERCISE 1

TWO-ARM CURLS

Coaching Points:

Palm up grip on the bar. Elbows in close proximity to, but not touching, the sides. Head up, torso erect. Attempt to pull the bar with a semi-circular motion high onto the chest. Keep the wrists locked.

Bar Height:

1. Thigh level.
2. Waist level.
3. Chest level.

Benefits:

FOOTBALL: More power in the biceps and "hugging" muscles of the chest. Increase in strength needed to go "skin-to-skin" in tackling. Increased control over the ball when tucked away by a ball-carrier.

BASKETBALL: Increase in distance in hook-shooting. More strength and grasping power in "tie-up" situations. Increase in power needed to control the ball on the way down after rebounding.

BASEBALL: Increase in strength required to accomplish a snap-throw (underarm). Greater power in the upper chest needed to hit the long ball. Greater grip strength in the hands and wrists necessary in hitting and throwing.

EXERCISE 2

REVERSE CURLS

Coaching Points:

Palm-down grips on the bar. Head up, torso erect. Elbows close to the sides but not touching. Wrists locked. Attempt to reverse-curl the bar with a semi-circular motion to a position high on the chest.

Bar Height:

1. Thigh level.
2. Waist level.
3. Chest level.

Benefits:

FOOTBALL: Increase in grip strength for centers, quarterbacks and ball carriers. Development of the forearm strength required for defense against blockers. (Forearm "shiver".) More power in the forearm and wrist in straight-arming.

BASKETBALL: Increase in forearm and grip strength required in rebounding. Stronger wrists for surer and quicker passes and shooting. Finger strength aids in controlling a dribble more effectively.

BASEBALL: More effective bat control through increase in grip strength. Quicker, more powerful forearms at contact with the ball in hitting.

EXERCISE 3

TRICEPS EXTENSIONS

Coaching Points:

Place the hands palms-down on the bar at shoulder width. Step through under the bar to the opposite side. Bring the elbows to a position in which they are *high and parallel.* This means that the upper arms are as close to the ears as possible. The wrists should be uncocked or "laid back." The position should closely approximate that assumed by a basketball player about to shoot a long one-handed shot. The arms should be extended overhead with a semi-circular motion, rather than a straight-up movement.

Bar Height:

1. Ear level.
2. Top of head.
3. 6″ above head.

Benefits:

FOOTBALL: Greater power, increased distance in a quarterback's passing. More speed developed in the center's long punting snap. Increase in a lineman's strength required to fend off blockers.

BASKETBALL: Greater power and distance in shooting. Quicker, sharper chest and bounce passes. The musculature developed through this exercise is *absolutely necessary* in these actions.

BASEBALL: Excellent developer of the throwing musculature. This exercise will also increase the strength needed at the moment of impact in hitting. (As the wrists begin to roll.)

EXERCISE 4

BAR WRINGING

Coaching Points:

Assume a position in which the hands are placed hands-down, approximately six to eight inches apart. The bar should be placed at shoulder level. The exercise is conducted in two segments:

A. On command, the performer attempts to turn his right wrist *down*, while the left attempts to turn away from him.

B. The exercise should be repeated with the left wrist moving down and the right wrist moving away from him.

In both of the contractions, the performer should be conscious of queezing the bar with the fingers *forcibly* while attempting to "wring" the bar.

Bar Height:

Usually shoulder level but may be varied slightly in workouts so that muscles are developed at different angles.

Benefits:

FOOTBALL: Beneficial to both centers and quarterbacks with regard to ball control.

BASKETBALL: The benefits here are obvious. Probably in no other team sport are so many members required to handle the ball. This necessitates a tremendous amount of strength in the fingers, which bar wringing can provide.

BASEBALL: Here again, in batting and throwing, we need the flexor strength which this exercise develops.

EXERCISE 5

MILITARY PRESS

Coaching Points:

Assume a position in which the legs provide a wide base. Elbows should be thrown slightly forward under the bar. With the knees locked, arch the back slightly and attempt to drive the bar *straight up* through the rack.

Bar Height:

1. Chin level.
2. Top of head.
3. Just before point at which arms are fully extended.

Benefits:

FOOTBALL: Develops musculature used in warding off blockers on defense, and straight-arming a tackler on offense. Increased distance and sharpness in passing for quarterbacks. Increased speed and distance in center's punting snap. Development of anterior deltoid also helps to prevent "knock-down" shoulders.

BASKETBALL: Increased distance in jump shooting. Quicker, sharper chest and bounce passes. Increase in strength needed to throw the long pass.

BASEBALL: Increase in strength of elbow extensors means more speed and distance in throwing. Increased speed in the swing to the point at which the wrists take over in hitting.

EXERCISE 6

WRIST CURLS

Coaching Points:

The performer should be in a seated position. The arms are placed in a palms-up position on top of the thighs. The wrists are placed on top of the knees so that the hands are free to move up and down. The bar is grasped with the wrists hyperextended. From this position, the performer attempts to curl the bar until the wrists are fully flexed, without raising the forearms from the legs.

Bar Height:

1. Below kneecap.
2. Even with kneecap.
3. Above kneecap.

Benefits:

FOOTBALL: Increase in grip strength aids in making tackles more secure.

BASKETBALL: Extremely valuable here since the musculature developed is the same as that required to 'snap the wrist" in shooting and dribbling.

BASEBALL: An excellent exercise to develop the throwing muscles of the forearm, wrist and hand. An increase in both speed and distance should result.

EXERCISE 7

SHOULDER PRESS

Coaching Points:

Subject assumes a position in which the bar is adjusted approximately 2-3 inches above shoulder height. The bar is positioned behind the performers head. The attempted movement is to force the bar straight up. Care should be taken at the outset of the program to emphasize the fact that in the first position, the contraction should build up slowly.

Bar Height:

1. Shoulder level.
2. Top of head.
3. 6″ above head.

Benefits:

FOOTBALL: Development of the extensors of the arms and shoulders. Excellent deterrent from the standpoint of shoulder injuries.

BASKETBALL: The all-important shooting and rebounding muscles are developed as a result of this exercise.

BASEBALL: Development of the upper arm and shoulder musculature will provide added power in throwing and hitting.

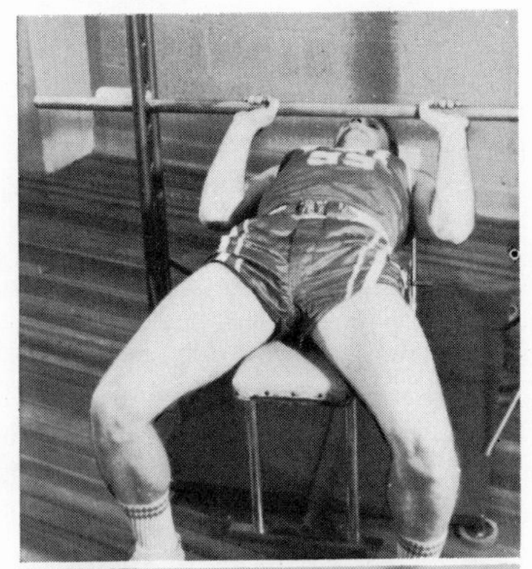

EXERCISE 8

BENCH (SUPINE) PRESS

Coaching Points:

The subject assumes a supine position. Both feet are placed flat on the floor to provide added stability. The hands are spread slightly wider than the width of the shoulders.

Bar Height:

1. 2″ above chest.
2. 8-10″ above chest.
3. Point just before arms are fully extended.

Benefits:

FOOTBALL: This is one of the best exercises known to develop the gross musculature of the chest, arms, and shoulders. More power in these areas will include a player's effectiveness as a lineman or a back.

BASKETBALL: Will aid in developing a performer into a more sturdy, more durable player. Development of this musculature will prove to be the difference between a boy who can be forced out of position under the basket, and one who has the physical equipment to hold his ground.

BASEBALL: Here we are concentrating on the "power" muscles of the upper arm, shoulder girdle and chest. All of these muscles contribute to more power in throwing and batting.

EXERCISE 9

UPRIGHT ROWING

Coaching Points:

The hands are placed six to eight inches apart with the palms facing downward. The movement is an attempted lift straight up the body to a point just below the chin. The elbows should remain in a "spread" position. Some boys may try to lean back in the first two positions, but this should be discouraged, since this technique involves musculature we are not attempting to develop here.

Bar Height:

1. Groin level.
2. Diaphragm level.
3. Shoulder level.

Benefits:

FOOTBALL: The shoulder elevators (deltoids) are the natural shoulder pads of the body. Through their development, we provide the athlete with a larger, stronger hitting area. In addition, the deltoids play an important role in driving the shoulder upward, contributing to sharper and harder initial contact in blocking and tackling.

BASKETBALL: The development of the muscles involved in this exercise will aid in preventing "arm weariness" associated with keeping the hands up on defense and in handling the ball.

BASEBALL: This exercise will not contribute a great deal specifically in baseball, but will certainly aid in all-around development of the shoulder.

EXERCISE 10

ALTERNATE GRIP EXERCISE

Coaching Points:

The bar should be placed slightly below shoulder level. An alternate grip is assumed with the hands, which are from three to five inches apart. The arms should maintain an extended position. The action here is to attempt to pronate the hand that is palm up, and to supinate the hand that is palm down. In other words, if the right hand is palm up, and the left hand is palm down, the performer should be attempting to turn the *right* hand over in a *left* direction, and the *left* hand over in a *left* direction. (Both turning in the same direction.)

Bar Height:

Shoulder level.

Benefits:

Football: This exercise is excellent for developing grip and forearm strength in the quarterbacks and ball carriers. The centers will also benefit, in that grip strength improves ball control on the snap.

Basketball: Stronger wrists and hands in rebounding, shooting, and dribbling.

Baseball: This exercise is extremely valuable in baseball. The pronators and supinators we are developing are essential in throwing, especially in pitching. The "screwball" and curve cannot be thrown effectively if the musculature is not fully developed.

EXERCISE 11

BAR TELESCOPING

Coaching Points:

The bar is placed at shoulder height. The hands are placed with a palms-down grip approximately at shoulder width. The feet are spread to shoulder width, with the knees locked. The exercise is done in two phases.

A. In the first contraction, the performer attempts to pull the ball apart in the middle. At the same time, he attempts to force his legs outward, keeping the feet flat on the floor and the knees locked.

B. In the second phase, reverse the procedure, attempting to telescope the bar into itself. At the same time, the attempt is made to draw the legs together. (Knees locked)

Bar Height:

Usually shoulder height but may be reset for variety.

Benefits:

FOOTBALL: A fine all-around developer of the large muscle groups used in football. We bring into play adductors and abductors of the arms and legs, all of which are important functioning groups in the sport. Special mention should be made of the fact that the adductor magnus is one of the most frequently "pulled" muscles in the body, and through conditioning and proper stretching we can help to alleviate this condition.

BASKETBALL: The shooting and passing muscles of the arms, chest and back all benefit from this exercise. In addition, the adductors and abductors are developed, making this a multiple exercise.

BASEBALL: The pectoralis, anterior and posterior deltoids, and associated shoulder girdle musculature so important in effective performance in throwing and hitting, make this an excellent baseball exercise.

EXERCISE 12

THROWING EXERCISE

Coaching Points:

This exercise should be done with the preferred arm. As will be noted in the illustrations, the actual throwing motion of the arm and body is duplicated in three positions. The exercise may also be modified for javelin and shot contestants.

Bar Height:

1. Ear level.
2. 6″ above head.
3. Point at which arm is almost fully extended.

Benefits:

FOOTBALL: This exercise is one which would have the greatest value if it were performed by quarterbacks. The accompanying photographs are slanted more toward baseball and basketball, but little modification is required to approximate a quarterback's throwing motion.

BASKETBALL: This exercise will permit your players to throw the clearing pass on the fast break more quickly and effectively. Regular passes will be sharper too.

BASEBALL: Here is probably one of the best exercises we have today for a baseball player. This is true because of the fact that we utilize the actual motion of throwing for our movement. In addition to the musculature of the arm used in throwing, we also involve the trunk rotators and hip flexors and extensors.

EXERCISE 13

REVERSE WRIST CURLS

Coaching Points:

The performer is seated, with the forearms placed flat against the thighs. The junction of the wrists should protrude three or four inches out over the knees. The palms are facing down when the grip is assumed. Keep the forearms *in* contact with the knees.

Bar Height:

1. Below kneecap.
2. Even with kneecap.
3. Above kneecap.

Benefits:

FOOTBALL: The extensors of the wrist and forearm are strengthened, enabling your lineman to defend themselves against an initial charge more effectively, thus preventing the blocker from establishing contact for that valuable extra second.

BASKETBALL: Wrist extensors are probably not as valuable as the flexors in basketball, but total development of the forearm will increase the ball control musculature.

BASEBALL: The same observation may be applied here as in basketball. Total development will increase the effectiveness of total performance.

EXERCISE 14

INCLINED PRESS

Coaching Points:

Performer should be in a half-reclining position or an inclined bench. (These may be made very easily if commercial ones are not included in present inventory.) Each workout period the angle of the backrest should be varied, so that the arm, shoulder and chest musculature may be more effectively exercised. Both feet should be flat on the floor. The bar should be forced upward at a 90° angle to the floor.

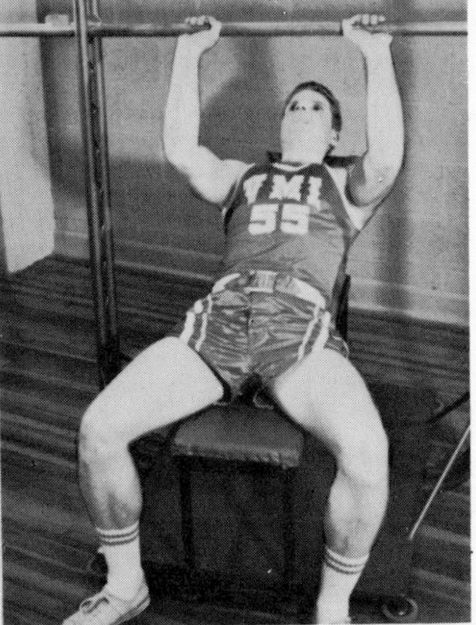

Bar Height:

1. Just above chest.
2. 8-10″ above chest.
3. Just before arms are extended.

Benefits:

FOOTBALL: This is an excellent developer of the triceps, anterior deltoids and pectoralis muscles. The importance played by these groups relative to line play cannot be overemphasized.

BASKETBALL: Longer jump and push shots, sharper passes, and more powerful "clutching" muscles used in rebounding may all result from the use of this exercise.

BASEBALL: Longer throws from outfielders and infielders, more speed in pitching, and the power needed to hit the ball farther are the expected benefits to be derived from this exercise in developing baseball players.

CHAPTER SEVEN

The Lower Extremities

Running, jumping, stopping, starting, changing direction, hurdling, climbing and walking . . . all important functions of the legs and hips.

These are readily apparent manifestations of large muscle groups. Less apparent are the constant and minute adjustments that smaller groups accomplish in maintaining posture and balance.

With these members responsible for so many functions, it goes without saying that the importance of proper development cannot be overly stressed. How do we usually go about it?

In all too many situations, the persons responsible for the total conditioning programs of athletes rely on a slightly vague system of wind sprints or long distance running. At this point, let me stress the fact that I am totally in favor of both of the above-mentioned methods of conditioning. They have a definite role to play in any training regimen as a supplemental activity.

I feel, however, that when these are the only methods employed in leg conditioning, then the trainer has been remiss.

When one stops to consider the fact of how little the legs are used in normal daily activity, we realize that more intensive work than mere running is indicated.

Remember walking to school? Maybe you were a little more modern, and parked your bike along with many others in a rack outside. In both cases, you used your legs for locomotion. Did you ever realize that when architects are drawing the blue prints for a modern high school, they must allot about twice as much space for the parking lot as for the actual physical plant? As we all know, teachers can't afford cars, so they must belong to the students. If they're riding, they can't be walking, and if they're not walking, there is very little leg development occurring.

In this chapter, we will deal with exercises designed to accomplish the total conditioning of this important aspect of the body.

EXERCISE 1

LEG CURL (STANDING)

Coaching Points:

The performer should support himself while exercising. The point of contact with the bar should be where the calcaneus joins the achilles tendon. The performer should attempt to move the bar through a semi-circular arc.

Bar Height:

1. Point at which the leg is almost fully extended.
2. Leg flexed at 45°.
3. Leg flexed at 90°.

Benefits:

FOOTBALL: Develops the "hamstring" group responsible for flexing the leg in running. Development, and proper stretching of this group will tend to prevent the "pulled hamstrings" so prevalent in athletics.

BASKETBALL: Same as above.

BASEBALL: Same as above.

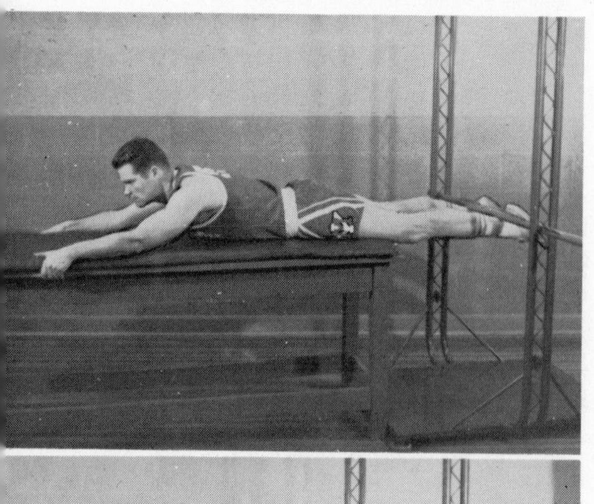

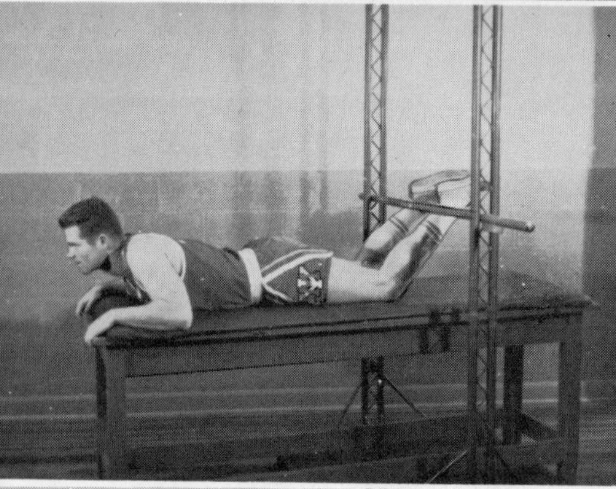

EXERCISE 2

LEG CURL (LYING)

Coaching Points:

Performer should be in a prone position, with hands or arms anchored under the table for stability. Exercise may be performed with both legs at the same time. Attempt should be made to move the bar to the buttocks in a semi-circular arc.

Bar Height:

1. Slightly above the level of the table. (No strain on knees.)
2. Legs flexed at 45°.
3. Legs flexed at 90°.

Benefits:

FOOTBALL: Essentially the same as Exercise 1, except that the elevating action of the lower back muscles is reduced in this position so that only the flexors of the leg are the prime movers.

BASKETBALL: Same as above.

BASEBALL: Same as above.

EXERCISE 3

HALF SQUAT

Coaching Points:

Technique is *extremely* important in this exercise. Do not allow the performer to flex the knees to any less than 90° at the joint. Caution the performer to keep his back *straight*, with the buttocks located well under the bar, so that small muscles of the back are not involved. The performer should attempt to drive the bar straight up through the rack by extending his legs.

Bar Height:

1. Point at which the knees are at 90°.
2. Knees flexed at about 130°.
3. Point at which the performer has the legs almost extended.

Benefits:

FOOTBALL: Firing out of the stance in the initial charge. Driving power after initial contact. General running. Leaping by defensive backs and linebackers. Develops extensors used in punting and place-kicking.

BASKETBALL: Gaining height on jump balls. Added height in rebounding. More drive in general running.

BASEBALL: Quicker starts and added speed in base running. Better "jump" on batted balls. Essential for pitchers in the leg pushing off the rubber.

EXERCISE 4

ADDUCTOR EXERCISE

Coaching Points:

Performer lies on his side and stabilizes by grasping the table. Legs should remain extended while the athlete forces directly downward on the bar. Bar may be padded if there is any discomfort.

Bar Height:

1. The working leg should begin at about a 75° angle.
2. 45°.
3. 25-30°.

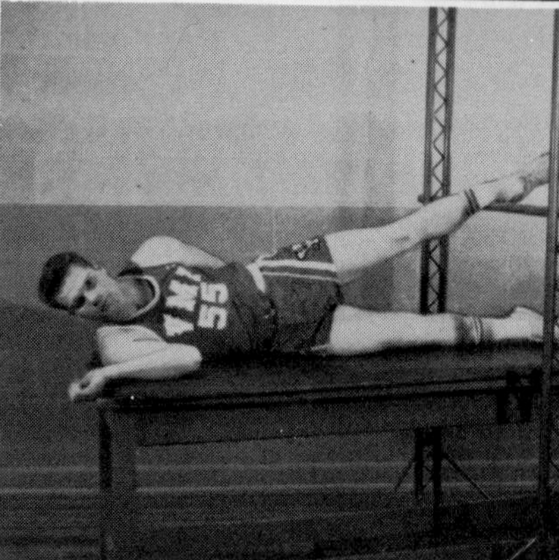

Benefits:

FOOTBALL: Development of this adductor muscle, combined with intelligent stretching will prevent many of the "pulled groins" common in athletics.

BASKETBALL: Same as above. Musculature is also used in any cross-over step, such as those used on defense.

BASEBALL: Same as above.

EXERCISE 5

ABDUCTOR EXERCISE

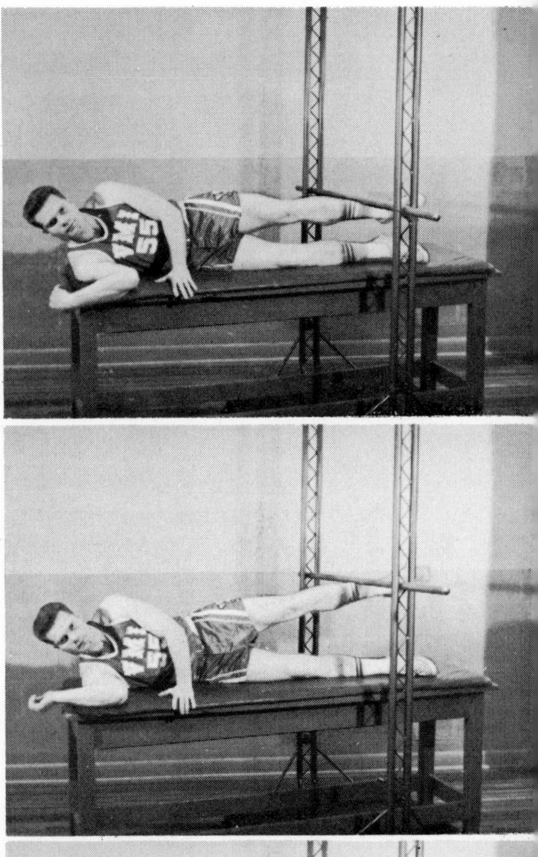

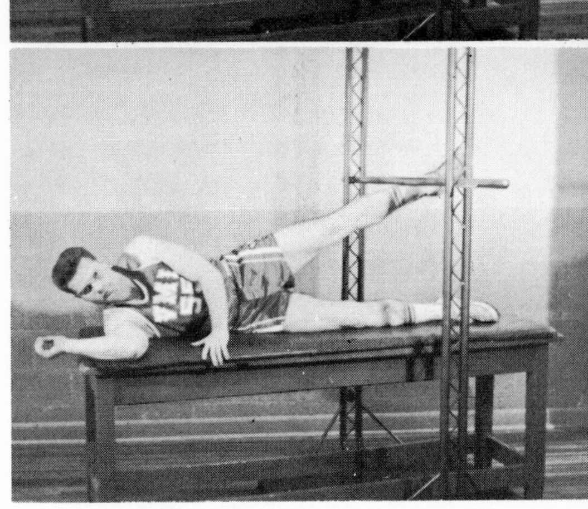

Coaching Points:

The technique is the same as the preceding exercise, except the performer will be forcing upward on the bar. Again, the bar may be padded. (The reverse of exercise 4.)

Bar Height:

1. 25-30°.
2. 45°.
3. 75°.

Benefits:

FOOTBALL: General development of the lateral aspects of the legs. Addition of bulk.

BASKETBALL: Same as above.

BASEBALL: Same as above.

EXERCISE 6

TOE RAISE

Coaching Points:

The performer should understand that he is attempting to elevate the bar simply by rising on his toes, and not by extending his legs. The knees should remain locked.

Bar Height:

The bar height should be adjusted for each man so that maximum resistance is felt by the athlete as he assumes the first, second and third positions. This may be accomplished by allowing the arms to play the role of the resistance in each case, so that minute adjustments are possible. Place a block under the performer's feet so that the heels are below the level of the toes in position 1.

Benefits:

FOOTBALL: Provides greater power in running. Helps to make the initial charge more powerful and quick. May develop greater jumping ability in defensive backs.

BASKETBALL: Valuable in strengthening the musculature used in rebounding and jump shooting.

BASEBALL: Increase in general running power. Valuable for pitchers as they develop power for toeing off rubber.

EXERCISE 7

LEG EXTENSIONS

Coaching Points:

Performer should stabilize by grasping the side of the rack. A pad or mat may be provided for the back. Legs should force straight up through the bar. The bar should be contacted across the insets.

Bar Height:

1. Legs bent slightly less than 90°.
2. Legs at 110-120°.
3. Legs at 150°.

Benefits:

FOOTBALL: Greater charging power in tackling and blocking.
BASKETBALL: Greater driving and jumping power.
BASEBALL: Increase in general running power and starts toward batted balls for fielders.

EXERCISE 8

LEG EXTENSORS (SEATED)

Coaching Points:

The legs should not be flexed to any more of an angle than 90°. The bar should be contacted at the top of the insteps, and padding may be provided here. The performer should lean back *just slightly* in his seated position, and try to extend upward and outward.

Bar Height:

1. Knees flexed at 90°.
2. Knees at 120°.
3. Knees at 150°.

Benefits:

FOOTBALL: Excellent place kicking and punting exercise.

BASKETBALL: Emphasis on quadriceps, the extensors of the legs necessary in jumping and running.

BASEBALL: Strengthening of this muscle group will provide additional stabilization of the knee and lessen the chance of injury in this area due to torque so common in baseball (and in fact, all sports).

EXERCISE 9

PUNTER'S EXERCISE

Coaching Points:

A rope should be attached to the rack to provide a point of stability for the performer. This will also allow the man to approximate the true punting motion as closely as possible. Bar may be padded, since the point of contact is against the top of the instep.

Bar Height:

1. 100-100° angle.
2. 130-150°.
3. 170-180°.

Benefits:

FOOTBALL: Increase in muscular power through the actual punting range. General development of legs as well.

BASKETBALL: General development and aid in stabilizing knee.

BASEBALL: General development and stabilization of knee.

EXERCISE 10

DUMMY SCISSOR

Coaching Points:
Although there is only one position in the exercise, it may be varied from workout to workout to provide greater development. For example, the point of pressure in PHOTO 10 A is at the knees. The next time it might be changed to the lower leg, and then to the thighs. Performer should lock ankles and squeeze with his maximum effort.

Bar Height:

Not applicable.

Benefits:

FOOTBALL: General development of medial aspects of the legs.

BASKETBALL: Same as above.

BASEBALL: Same as above.

EXERCISE 11

PLACE KICKING EXERCISE

Coaching Points:

Performer should actually try his kicking motion a few times and then approximate this action as closely as possible with the placement of the bar in the exercise. He may stabilize by holding on to the sides of the rack.

Bar Height:

1. Knee at 90° angle.
2. Knee at 140°.
3. Knee at 170°. (Soccer-style kickers should modify positions to suit their kicking action.)

Benefits:

FOOTBALL: Development of musculature used in placement kicking for increased power and distance.

BASKETBALL: Primarily a football exercise, but may be used for general development of legs.

BASEBALL: Same as above.

EXERCISE 12

JEFFERSON LIFT

Coaching Points:

The performer straddles the bar, and takes an alternate grip with the hands. The action involved is to raise the bar to crotch level, concentrating on the action of the legs. Keep the back straight throughout the contractions.

Bar Height:

1. Knees flexed at 90°.
2. Knees flexed at 120°.
3. Knees flexed at 160-170°.

Benefits:

FOOTBALL: Development of power in the legs in blocking and tackling.

BASKETBALL: Development of rebounding power.

BASEBALL: General running power and quick starting ability.

EXERCISE 13

HIP EXTENSOR EXERCISE

Coaching Points:

The performer lies in a prone position and anchors himself by grasping the underside of the table. The point of contact with the bar is at the base of the ankle. The movement to be attempted is initiated in the low back and upper legs.

Bar Height:

1. The bar should be set so that the legs form a 120° angle with the table.
2. Legs at 140-150°.
3. Legs at 180°.

Benefits:

FOOTBALL: Development of those muscles used in straightening after making initial contact in blocking and tackling.

BASKETBALL: Facilitates movement in the flexed position used in defensive guarding and maneuvering with the ball.

BASEBALL: General strength in the low back and hamstring area.

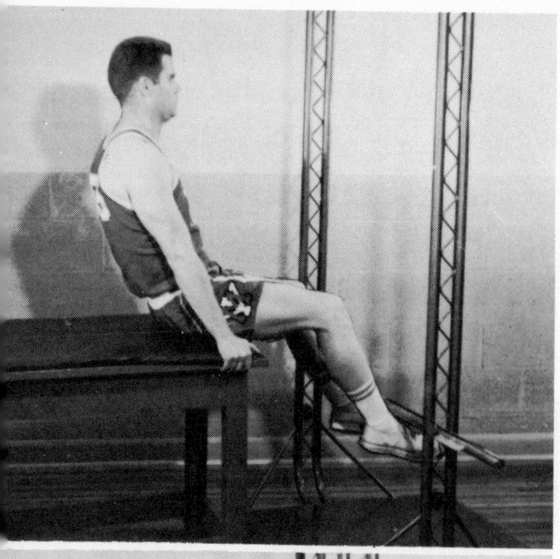

EXERCISE 14

HIP FLEXOR EXERCISE

Coaching Points:

Performer seated and grasping the underside of the table. The movement is to raise the bar in a perpendicular line while maintaining the flexed knee position. Point of contact is the top of the instep.

Bar Height:

1. Lowest point at which the leg hangs naturally with the knee flexed at 90°.
2. Six inches above this point.
3. Ten-Twelve inches above the original position.

Benefits:

FOOTBALL: Development of musculature necessary in general running, and especially for the "high knee" stride of a running back.

BASKETBALL: General leg development.

BASEBALL: General leg development.

EXERCISE 15

ANKLE EXERCISES

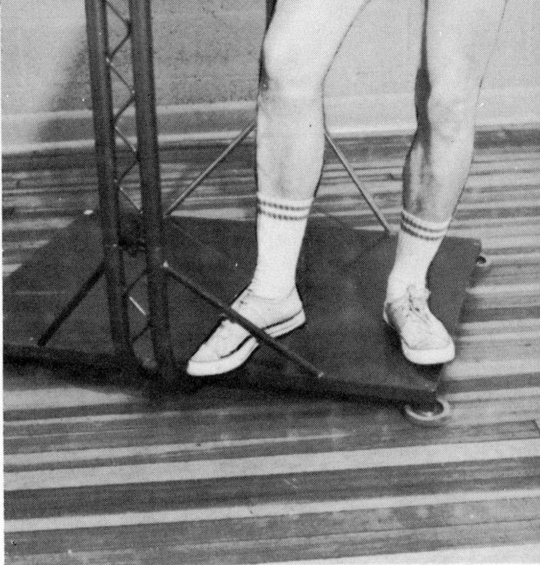

Coaching Points:

A. Performer assumes the position shown in Photo 15 A and attempts to flex the ankle against the resistance of the bar. He then places the bottom of the foot on the bar and attempts to extend the ankle downward.

B. Performer assumes the position in Photo 15 B. He then attempts to invert the ankle against the resistance of the upright. Next he should place the outside border of the foot against the support and attempt to evert the ankle. Both A and B should be repeated with the left foot.

Bar Height:

Lowest position on the rack.

Benefits:

FOOTBALL: Extremely valuable in developing ankle strength for general running. Additional benefit of developing musculature for prevention of ankle injuries. May be used as a remedial or rehabilitative exercise should an injury occur.

BASKETBALL: Development of musculature used in vertical jumping.

BASEBALL: Same benefits as those described above for football and basketball.

EXERCISE 16

DEAD LIFT (KNEES FLEXED)

Coaching Points:

Care should be exercised here relative to cautioning the performer to maintain a flexed-knee position. In this manner, the greatest force will be applied by the quadriceps rather than the smaller low back muscles.

Bar Height:

1. Position at which the knees are flexed at 90°.
2. Knees at an angle of 120°.
3. Knees flexed at 150-160°.

Benefits:

FOOTBALL: Extremely valuable in development of extensors used in "firing out" of a stance. More power in initial charge.

BASKETBALL: More power and height in vertical jumping.

BASEBALL: General leg development with the concomitant benefit of development of torso musculature.

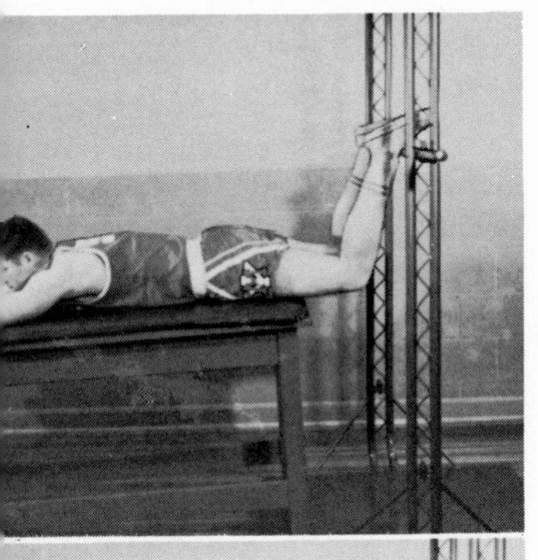

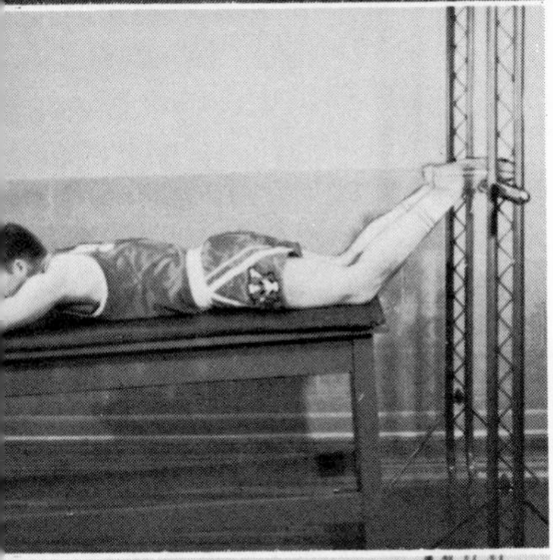

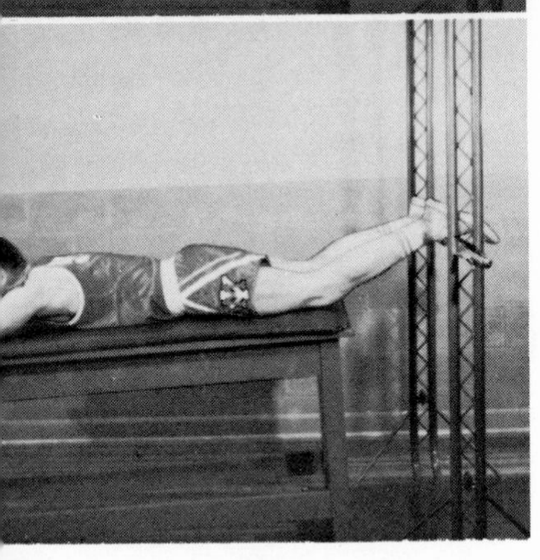

EXERCISE 17

DOLPHIN EXERCISE

Coaching Points:

Performer lying prone with the hands grasping the underside of the table. Point of contact with the bar should be on the top of the instep. Bar may be padded for comfort. Performer should attempt to extend the lower legs downward in a semicircular arc.

Bar Height:

1. Position at which the knees are flexed at 90°.
2. Knees at 150°.
3. Knees flexed at only a slight angle.

Benefits:

FOOTBALL: Valuable exercise in the development of musculature which aids in the stabilization of the knee. Good remedial exercise for post-operative knee injury cases.

BASKETBALL: Development of quadriceps, used in jumping vertically.

BASEBALL: Development of musculature needed for quicker, more explosive starts and general running speed.

CHAPTER EIGHT

The Back

In most conditioning programs, stress is placed upon the development of the arms, legs and shoulders, but relatively little attention is accorded the area to which this chapter is devoted.

For some reason, we seem to consider the back as a simple supporting structure, rather than a movable, highly diversified area essential in athletic performance.

We are afflicted with a great deal of back ailments in this country. In fact, the comparison of symptoms and complaints is fast becoming an indoor sport. A great amount of these ailments may be traced directly to poor postural habits acquired during our early formative years. Slouching and slumping over a period of years contributes directly to later discomfort. A strong back can be a tremendous asset in preventing this malady.

When we consider the back in relation to athletics, we should be acutely aware of the added importance that back strength assumes. The stresses and demands placed upon this area become readily apparent if one considers the movements involved in almost any sport carefully. This, of course, is especially true in a contact sport such as football.

In order to satisfy our responsibility to our athletes, our training regimen should include some of the exercises described in this chapter. The inclusion of these exercises will produce a more finely conditioned, more powerful athlete, less susceptible to low back injuries and strains.

EXERCISE 1

DEAD LIFT

Coaching Points:

Since the area developed by this exercise is one which is not *normally* a strong one, care must be taken in the performance of the exercise. Rather than contracting at his maximum, the athlete should be instructed to use 2/3 power for a week or so. The movement involved is to attempt to straighten the back until the torso is erect and the bar at thigh level.

Bar Height:

1. Bar at ankle level.
2. Bar at knee level.
3. Bar at thigh level.

Benefits:

FOOTBALL: Development of musculature needed in "lifting a tackle" or forcing upward on a block.

BASKETBALL: Development of muscles used for stability and strength at the top of the stretch in rebounding and shooting.

BASEBALL: General power in throwing and hitting, with the added benefit of conditioning to prevent injury due to strain in this area.

EXERCISE 2

VERTICAL LIFT (FLEXED POSITION)

Coaching Points:

The performer should be aware of the importance of proper position. Feet well spread, with knees locked. Since the exercise involves the extensors of the trunk, (muscles not usually subjected to great stress) it would be advisable to have the athletes contract at less than maximum for a few workouts until a modicum of strength is developed. The attempt should be to force the bar upward and outward.

Bar Height:

1. Halfway between knee and ankle.
2. Knee height.
3. Waist height.

Benefits:

FOOTBALL: Excellent in developing those muscles responsible for "lifting" a tackle, or working upward after the initial contact in a block.

BASKETBALL: Strength developed in the low back; area of great stress in rebounding and tie-up situations.

BASEBALL: General development and addition of strength in an area susceptible to injury.

EXERCISE 3

POSTERIOR LATERAL RAISES

Coaching Points:

The arm should remain locked at the elbow throughout the exercise. The legs should be straight, with the back parallel to the floor throughout all three positions. The attempt against the bar is upward. The exercise should be repeated with the left arm.

Bar Height:

1. Knee height.
2. Groin level.
3. Waist height.

Benefits:

FOOTBALL: Good conditioner of the abductors of the arms. Strength developed for tackling and stabilization of the shoulder.

BASKETBALL: General posterior shoulder development for strength in rebounding. Also develops musculature used in cross-chest passing and outlet passes on fast break.

BASEBALL: Excellent exercise for hitters, developing muscles of the shoulder and back used all through the swing, and especially at impact.

EXERCISE 4

BENT-OVER ROWING

Coaching Points:

Although it may feel unnatural for the performer, he should keep the back parallel to the floor during all positions. An extremely wide base is desirable. It will help the athlete to use proper technique if he is told to bend the arms slightly in all positions. This will prevent him from using the small extensors of the trunk. The lift should be made primarily with the arms.

Bar Height:

1. Lowest position on the rack.
2. Shin height.
3. Knee height.

Benefits:

FOOTBALL: Great development of "squeezing" musculature used in tackling. Stabilization of shoulder, resulting in increased strength in "arm tackles".

BASKETBALL: Development of musculature essential in strong ball control while rebounding and faking with the ball.

BASEBALL: Development of shoulder depressors necessary in achieving a stronger, quicker arm for throwing.

EXERCISE 5

ANTERIOR RAISE

Coaching Points:

Wide base, legs locked, torso erect. The attempt should be made to raise the bar to shoulder level, forcing upward and outward.

Bar Height:

1. Hip height.
2. Waist height.
3. Chest height.

Benefits:

FOOTBALL: Excellent all-around development of the deltoids, essential in protection of the shoulder in blocking and tackling. Stabilization of the shoulder.

BASKETBALL: Good developer of musculature used in hook shooting. Strengthening of muscles used in defensive arm position in guarding.

BASEBALL: General development of deltoids (including posterior aspects) used in both the throwing and hitting movements.

EXERCISE 6

POSTERIOR RAISE

Coaching Points:

Extremely wide base is necessary for stabilizing. The performer will have to adjust his relation to the rack for positions two and three. A slight forward lean of the torso is advisable for comfort.

Bar Height:

1. Thigh height.
2. Small of the back.
3. Just below the shoulder blades.

Benefits:

FOOTBALL: Valuable in developing musculature used in shedding a blocker (for both backs and linemen).

BASKETBALL: Cross chest passes and fast break outlet passing musculature.

BASEBALL: Development of musculature which comes into play during "power phase" of the hitters swing.

EXERCISE 7

HACK LIFT

Coaching Points:

Performer should be cautioned to assume a flexed-knee position, and to perform the lift with the assistance of the legs. The attempt should be made to lift in a *strictly vertical* direction.

Bar Height:

1. Ankle height.
2. Knee height.
3. Thigh height.

Benefits:

FOOTBALL: Good development of leg and back muscles used in firing out on a block, or in making initial contact on a tackle.

BASKETBALL: Development of leg and back muscles used in extending vertically as in rebounding.

BASEBALL: General developer of legs and low back for quick starts in base running or fielding.

EXERCISE 8

ROWING EXERCISE

Coaching Points:

Instruct the athlete to lean backward as he contracts so that he will not raise himself off the ground. The attempt to pull the bar toward the performer should be made with sum total of the arms, legs and the back.

Bar Height:

The same for all positions. The athlete should vary his own position to correspond with the photos.

Benefits:

FOOTBALL: Development of power in the low back and legs necessary for strong, sure tackling and blocking.

BASKETBALL: Development of areas used in rebounding. (Legs, back and arms.)

BASEBALL: Development of back and leg musculature provides more power in hitting and throwing.

EXERCISE 9

BAR BREAKING EXERCISE

Coaching Points:

Extremely wide grip on the bar, with the hands placed palm down. The bar should be padded at the point where the knee contacts the bar.

Bar Height:

Thigh level.

Benefits:

FOOTBALL: Development of shoulder depressors used in hand fighting and shedding blockers.

BASKETBALL: Development of muscles used in controlling the ball after rebounding. Helps to prevent steals.

BASEBALL: Development of musculature used in hitting and throwing.

EXERCISE 10

BOW AND ARROW EXERCISE

Coaching Points:

The lead arm should provide the stabilizing factor on the bar. This arm is always in a fully extended position. The attempt involved should be the action of "drawing" a bow.

Bar Height:

Shoulder level.

Benefits:

FOOTBALL: Stabilization of the shoulder in blocking and tackling positions. Development of strength in forearm lift.

BASKETBALL: General shoulder and upper back development.

BASEBALL: Development of musculature to provide more power in the impact of a hitting swing.

EXERCISE 11

ONE-ARMED PRESS

Coaching Points:

The legs are spread wide to form a solid base. The free hand is placed on the knee. The effort should be made to force the bar directly upward, utilizing the total force of the free hand pushing on the knee, the working arm forcing upward, and the trunk attempting to straighten.

Bar Height:

1. Shoulder level.
2. Six inches above position 1.
3. Twelve inches above position 2.

Benefits:

FOOTBALL: Development of extensors used in hand fighting. Trunk and low back development used in blocking and tackling means increased power.

BASKETBALL: Added strength in shoulder, back, and arm musculature essential in shooting and passing.

BASEBALL: Added distance and power in throwing. Development of back musculature used in hitting.

EXERCISE 12

REVERSE JACK-KNIFE

Coaching Points:

The performer should stabilize himself by grasping either side of the rack. The point of contact is at the back of the ankles. The bar should be padded. The attempt is to force the bar upward and away from the athlete in a semi-circular motion.

Bar Height:

1. Legs at 45° angle.
2. Legs at 60° angle.
3. Legs at 80° angle.

Benefits:

FOOTBALL: Development of low back musculature to aid in preventing injuries to this area.

BASKETBALL: General low back development. Added benefit in strengthening of hip extensors used in vertical jumping.

BASEBALL: General low back development.

EXERCISE 13

TRUNK RAISE (PRONE)

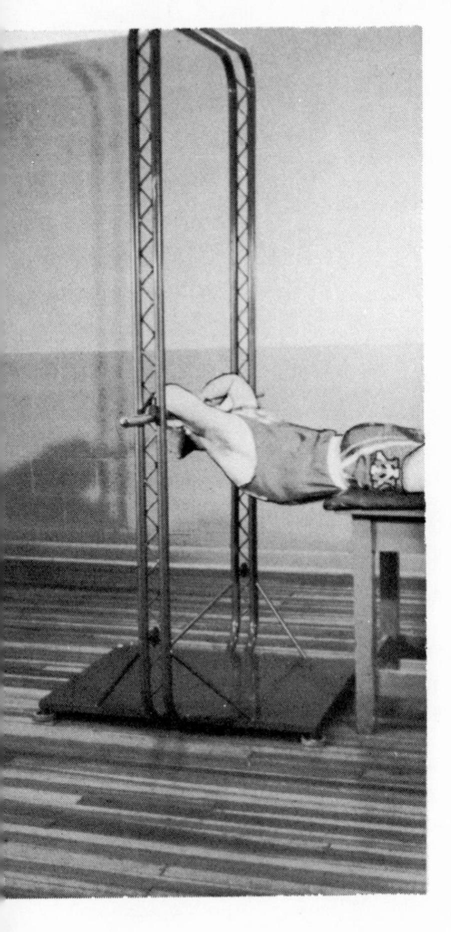

Coaching Points:

A one position exercise. The performer should be anchored at the heels either by a strap or by another athlete. The hands should be draped over the bar or folded behind the head to negate any action from them. It is recommended that the bar definitely be padded in this exercise. The performer attempts to extend the trunk upward against the bar.

Bar Height:

Ten to twelve inches above the top of the table.

Benefits:

FOOTBALL: Fine developer of musculature used in "working up" on a block. Also develops the lifting muscles used in tackling.

BASKETBALL: General development of low back, aiding in prevention of injury.

BASEBALL: Same as above.

EXERCISE 14

POSTERIOR HAND SEPARATOR

Coaching Points:

Although the first position is accomplished with extended arms, the bar should be raised in Positions 2 and 3 so that the arms are flexed. The performer attempts to separate the bar in the middle by forcing outward with both hands.

Bar Height:

1. Hip height.
2. Small of the back.
3. Four to five inches above Position 2.

Benefits:

FOOTBALL: General development of the back, but especially beneficial in developing the upper portions used in blocking positions.

BASKETBALL: More powerful shoulders, especially in rebounding.

BASEBALL: All-around development of back muscles necessary for the generation of more power in the hitting swing.

EXERCISE 15

REAR PRESS

Coaching Points:

The arms should be flexed slightly in all three positions. The attempt is to pull the bar backward over the head. A wide base should be used to insure stability.

Bar Height:

1. Eye level.
2. Top of the head.
3. Six inches above head.

Benefits:

FOOTBALL: Strengthens muscles used in forearm lifts and general blocking.

BASKETBALL: Develops musculature used in hook passes and hook shots.

BASEBALL: General development of a stronger upper back.

EXERCISE 16

BASEBALL SWING EXERCISE

Coaching Points:

As may be seen in the photographs, a towel or strap is used to simulate a bat. The towel allows the performer to assume any position in relation to the rack that he wishes. The actual movement of swinging a bat should be approximated as closely as possible.

Bar Height:

May be varied from the thighs to the shoulders in various workouts to simulate low and high pitches.

Benefits:

FOOTBALL: Good exercise for passers and backs. Develops rotating muscles of the torso. Also strengthens shoulder girdle.

BASKETBALL: Develops musculature used in long passes (full court type). Also strengthens muscles used in "fade" shots.

BASEBALL: Obviously an excellent method of developing musculature associated with the whole swing. A multiple exercise, involving arms, legs, hands, and torso.

EXERCISE 17

TABLE RAISE

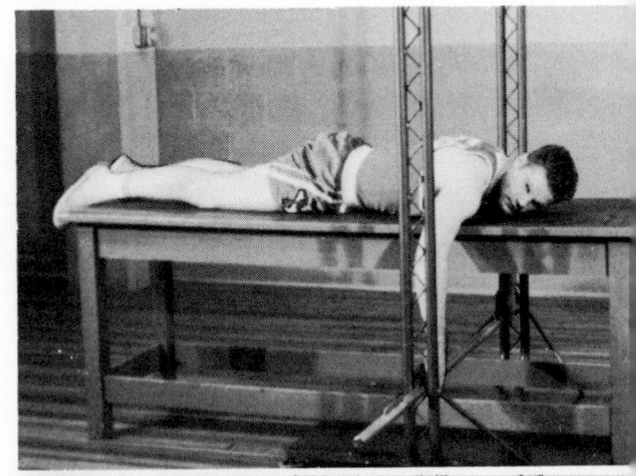

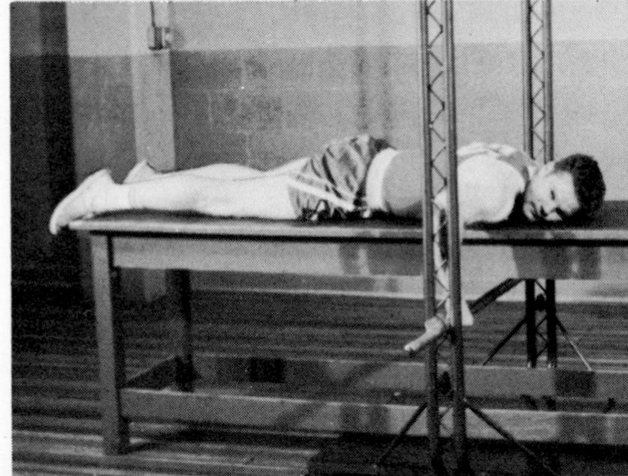

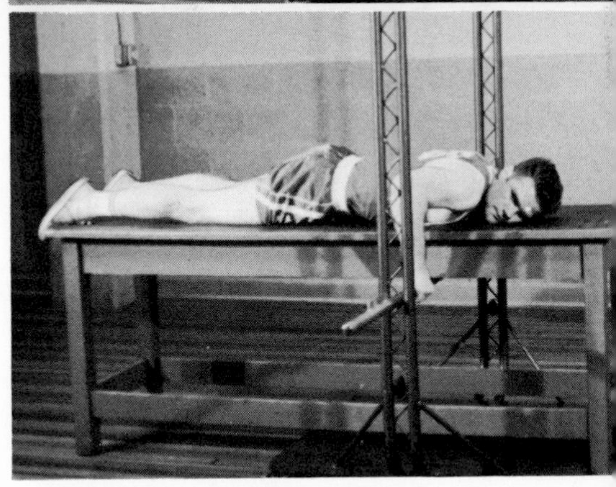

Coaching Points:

The table should be placed *over* the bar as shown in the photos. The head should be turned to one side to prevent discomfort. The attempt should be made to pull the bar to the chest.

Bar Height:

1. Arms fully extended.
2. Arms at 45°.
3. Just below the table.

Benefits:

FOOTBALL: Stability of shoulder in blocking and tackling positions.

BASKETBALL: Development of strength in areas needed for ball control in rebounding.

BASEBALL: General development of upper back to increase power in the hitting swing.

CHAPTER NINE

The Chest and Abdomen

SIZE – As coaches, we are all concerned with the size of our competing athletes. We want our football teams to be bigger and more rugged, our basketball players to be substantial and solid under the boards, and our baseball players to be larger and more powerful.

I do not mean to imply here that I subscribe to the theory that in order to be an athlete, one must possess above-average physical stature. Our experiences in athletics belie such an assumption.

There is definitely a place in athletics for the good little man. Quickness, speed, agility, timing and coordination are all attributes generally associated with this type of athlete. Moreover, the desirable qualities have usually been developed by the individual to a high degree in order that he might compete on a relatively even basis with the larger boys.

In the final analysis, however, much as we sometimes are reluctant to admit it, the old adage concerning a good big man beating a good small one is generally true. The premise, of course, has to be based on the assumption that both possess the same degree of competitive spirit, and that both are conditioned to the fullest capabilities of their muscle mass.

We can do little about the height of our raw material. No one has yet invented a rack for stretching a four foot five inch athlete. Mother Nature is entirely in command of this situation.

Weight or bulk is another matter altogether. A boy may be as tall as others his age and still appear to be small due to lack of bulk. Here is an area in which we can give Mother Nature a helping hand.

Whenever we "size" athletes visually, our attention is usually drawn to the torso or trunk of the body. Add weight and bulk to this area, and you have definitely affected an athlete's physical stature. He becomes more solid and less likely to be moved around easily by force on an athletic field.

In this chapter, the exercises are designed to develop the strength and bulk of the chest and abdominal muscles necessary in initiating and carrying out a great number of movements involved in athletics.

One last word concerning the abdomen. Regardless of whether you are attempting to condition individuals for a contact or non-contact sport, the abdomen should not be neglected. Well conditioned abdominal muscles are essential for good health. Exercise in this area stimulates the vital organs responsible for secreting and excreting essential fluids and materials so necessary for our well-being. The assistance that these muscles provide in maintaining good posture is also a primary consideration in dealing with young, physically immature athletes.

Select from the following chapter those exercises applicable to your sport that will provide the athlete with the bulk and strength needed in the torso, and those that will allow him to attain a conditioned mid-section.

EXERCISE 1

LATERAL RAISES (SUPINE)

Coaching Points:

The arms should remain straight throughout the exercise. The non-working hand should provide the anchor for the performer by its grasp under the table. The attempt is to lift the bar inward and upward to a 90° angle. The exercise should be repeated with the alternate arm.

Bar Height:

1. At position to which the arm can reach downward comfortably.
2. Even with the height of the table.
3. Arm at near the 90° angle.

Benefits:

FOOTBALL: Increased strength in grasping power for tackling. Added strength and power for shedding blockers.

BASKETBALL: Development of muscles necessary in hook passing and shooting. Greater gripping power for rebounding.

BASEBALL: Increased distance and power in throwing.

EXERCISE 2

THE RACK

Coaching Points:

The arms should remain extended in all positions. The performer may feel a great deal of stress in the first position during the initial workouts. If this is the case, instruct him to contract at less than maximum initially, gradually increasing the effort as he becomes acclimated to the exercise. The attempt is to force the arms together.

Bar Height:

May remain at shoulder height, but it is recommended that the position be varied from workout to workout in order to develop the musculature at varying angles.

Benefits:

FOOTBALL: Extremely valuable in strengthening the musculature which will prevent shoulder separations. Increased power in initial contact in tackling.

BASKETBALL: Develops greater distance in passing and shooting. Increased grip strength in ball handling.

BASEBALL: Increase in power for throwing. Greater strength in adductors for hitting.

EXERCISE 3

DUMMY SQUEEZE

Coaching Points:

Although the exercise makes use of a blocking dummy, variations are possible. During one workout, have the performer contact the dummy with his forearms for the effort. During another, make him use the elbows; then the upper arms may be used in still another workout. A maximum effort should be made to squeeze the arms through the dummy.

Bar Height:

Not applicable.

Benefits:

FOOTBALL: Increase in chest and arm strength necessary for surer tackles.

BASKETBALL: General development of arms and torso.

BASEBALL: Increase in strength in the shoulders, particularly those muscles which bring the arm forward, as in throwing and pitching.

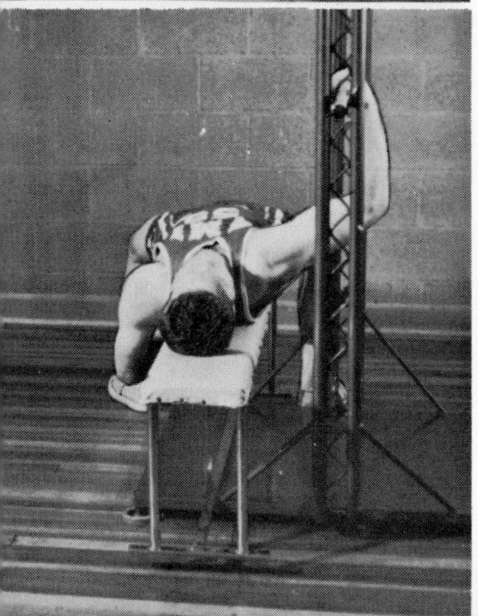

EXERCISE 4

LATERAL RAISES (SUPINE AND FLEXED)

Coaching Points:

The arms should be slightly flexed in the first position. The degree of flexion should be increased in position 2 and 3. The effort in the first two positions should be directed upward and inward, with the effort in 3 being directed inward and downward. Repeat with the alternate arm.

Bar Height:

1. Position at which the arms can reach downward comfortably and still remain flexed.
2. 8-10 inches above the table.
3. 24 inches above the table.

Benefits:

FOOTBALL: Increase in grasping strength. Excellent for quarterbacks and centers for throwing and snapping.

BASKETBALL: Greater rebounding arm strength. Increased hook passing and shooting power.

BASEBALL: Increase in chest and arm strength. Especially valuable in throwing and pitching.

EXERCISE 5

CROSS-OVER

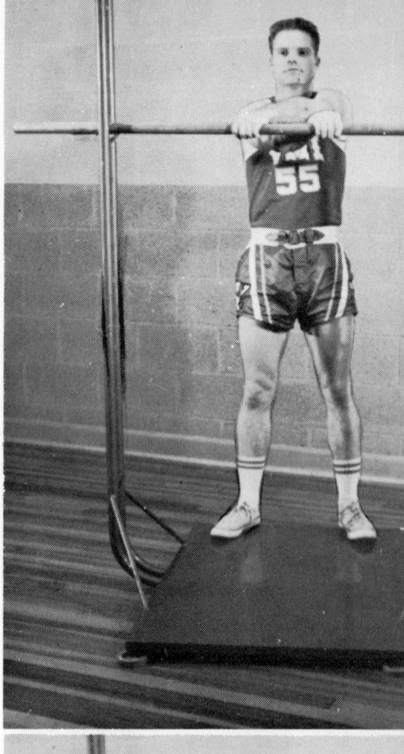

Coaching Points:

FOOTBALL: Excellent for quarterbacks The performer should cross one hand over the other with a palms-down grip. The attempt should be to force the right hand to the left, and the left hand in a right direction. In the first position the hands are in close proximity, and in the second they are separated by approximately six inches.

Bar Height:

May be varied, but limits should be set at shoulder height and waist height.

Benefits:

and centers in improving hand and forearm strength, in addition to developing the pectoralis minor essential in throwing and snapping the ball.

BASKETBALL: Increase in passing and shooting power, with the added benefit of improving hand and forearm strength for ball control.

BASEBALL: Great developer of musculature used in pitching and throwing. Added forearm strength provides better bat control in hitting.

EXERCISE 6

SUPINE STRAIGHT ARM CURL

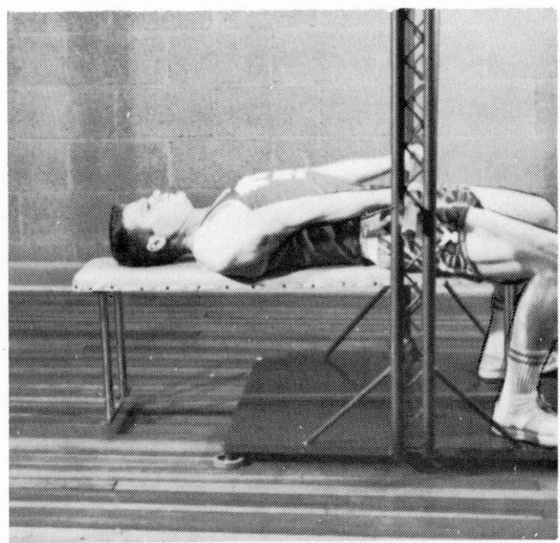

Coaching Points:

The arms should remain extended throughout the three positions. The hands are palm up. The attempt is to pull the bar upward to a position over the head.

Bar Height:

1. Position at which the arms are relatively parallel to the table top.
2. Arms at a 45° angle.
3. Arms at slightly less than 90°.

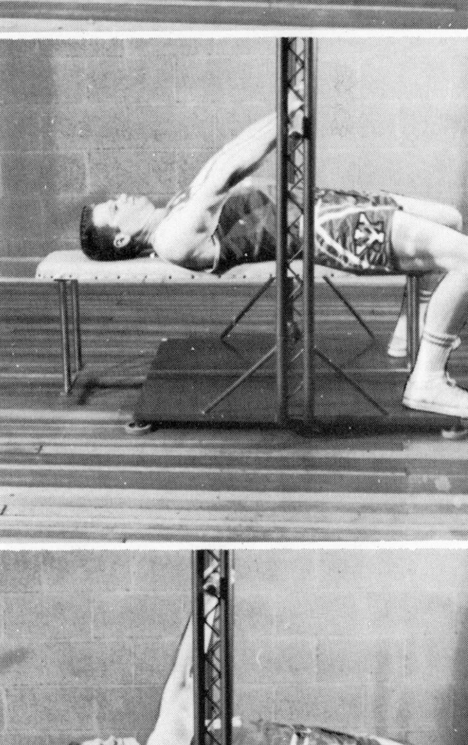

Benefits:

FOOTBALL: Stabilization of the shoulder for injury prevention. Development of forearm lift and hand fighting musculature.

BASKETBALL: General shoulder and chest development. Good exercise to develop bulk.

BASEBALL: Good exercise in developing the muscles needed in the sidearm and underarm throws. Shoulder and chest development.

EXERCISE 7

THORACIC EXPANDER

Coaching Points:

The performer should hang in a relaxed position initially. The lungs are then filled to maximum capacity and the position is held for six seconds. Repeat this process three to four cycles.

Bar Height:

Chinning height.

Benefits:

FOOTBALL: Because the intercostal muscles and the musculature associated with deep breathing are forced to work maximally against gravity, their development will tend to increase the thoracic capacity. This will assist the athlete in increasing his vital capacity for strenuous activity.

BASKETBALL: Same as above.

BASEBALL: Same as above.

EXERCISE 8

DISCUS EXERCISE

Coaching Points:

A demonstration of proper technique by the coach might be of value in this instance. The performer should imagine that he is actually going to "throw" the bar with a discus motion. A wide base with the feet and legs is essential for stability.

Bar Height:

1. Knee height.
2. Waist height.
3. Shoulder height.

Benefits:

FOOTBALL: Excellent quarterback exercise. Also of great value to lineman, as it develops the rotating muscles of the torso used in blocking and tackling.

BASKETBALL: Good exercise to develop passing and shooting musculature of the torso.

BASEBALL: Development of the rotators of the trunk is a great aid in providing more power in both hitting and throwing.

EXERCISE 9

HANGING LEVER

Coaching Points:

The arms must *remain straight*. The legs are kept in an extended position and are slowly raised to the 90° position which is held for six seconds. This exercise may be difficult at first, but with some slight assistance by a buddy during the first week or so, the athlete will be able to maintain the position without anyone "coaxing" his legs into position.

Bar Height:

Chinning height.

Benefits:

FOOTBALL: General development of abdominal section for better protection in contact.

BASKETBALL: General development of abdomen, essential in efficient athletic performance.

BASEBALL: General development of abdomen, essential in efficient athletic performance.

EXERCISE 10

SIDE BENDERS

Coaching Points:

Careful attention must be paid to proper technique in this particular exercise. The performer should lock both legs, and apply pressure outward with the leg closest to the bar. The attempt should be to *lean* away from the bar, while keeping the arm straight. Do not try to "pick the bar up." Repeat with the alternate arm.

Bar Height:

1. 8 inches below waist height.
2. 2 inches below waist level.

Benefits:

FOOTBALL: Development of rotators and flexors of the trunk provides the athlete with a stronger torso in blocking, faking, and tackling.

BASKETBALL: General development of midsection allows the player to fake, twist and rotate with more strength and speed. Especially useful for rebounders.

BASEBALL: Development of this musculature provides protection and strength in rotating in the swinging and throwing motions.

EXERCISE 11

TRUNK EXTENSIONS

Coaching Points:

The performer should extend both arms above his head, and then assume his position on the bar. Both legs should be locked. The attempt should be to push the bar up and away from the body, utilizing only the trunk muscles. Repeat to the opposite side.

Bar Height:

1. One foot above head.
2. 20-24 inches above head.

Benefits:

FOOTBALL: Development of musculature necessary in flexion and extension of trunk. These muscles are used constantly in blocking and tackling.

BASKETBALL: General development of muscles used in rebounding, shooting, and driving.

BASEBALL: Good developer of trunk muscles used in batting, and especially useful for hitters.

EXERCISE 12

SUPINE LEG RAISES

Coaching Points:

The legs should both be extended. The point of contact with the bar should be the top of the arch of the foot. The attempt should be to force the bar upward.

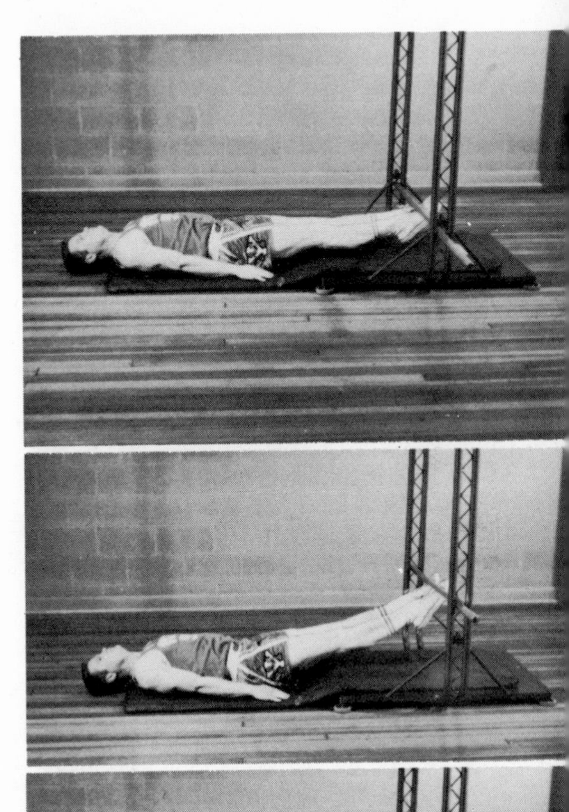

Bar Height:

1. Feet six inches from the floor.
2. Feet eighteen inches above the floor.
3. Feet thirty-six inches from the floor.

Benefits:

FOOTBALL: Strength development of abdominal musculature for protection in contact.

BASKETBALL: General abdominal development aids in creating a fully developed athlete.

BASEBALL: Same as above.

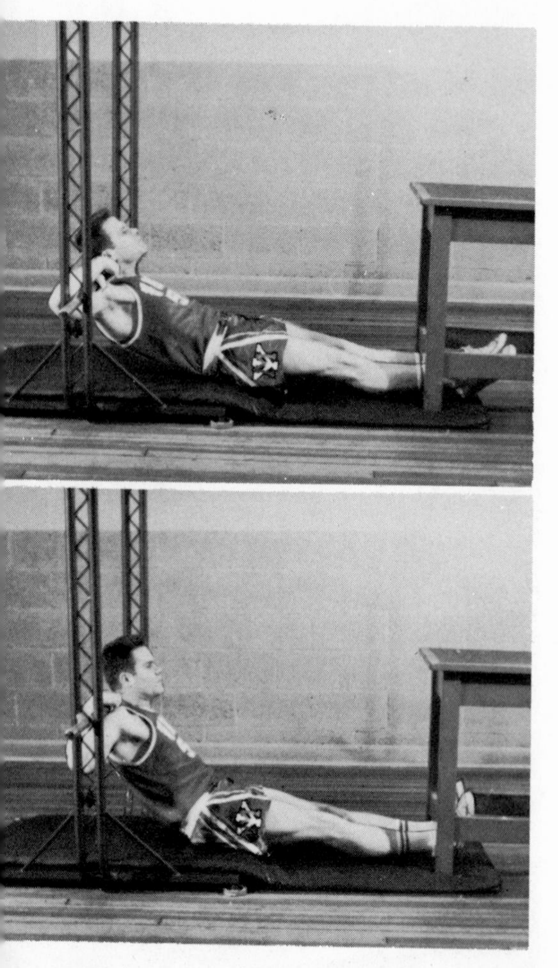

EXERCISE 13

SIT-UPS (LEGS EXTENDED)

Coaching Points:

An assist is needed here, either from a buddy or from a stable object. The hands should be clasped around the bar and back of the head. The attempt is to sit up against the resistance of the bar.

Bar Height:

1. Performer's head six inches above the floor.
2. The performer's head twelve inches above the floor.
3. Performer's head eighteen inches above the floor.

Benefits:

FOOTBALL: Development of abdominal muscles in the region above the waist provides greater strength and protection in contact.

BASKETBALL: General development in abdomen results in a stronger all-around athlete.

BASEBALL: Same as above.

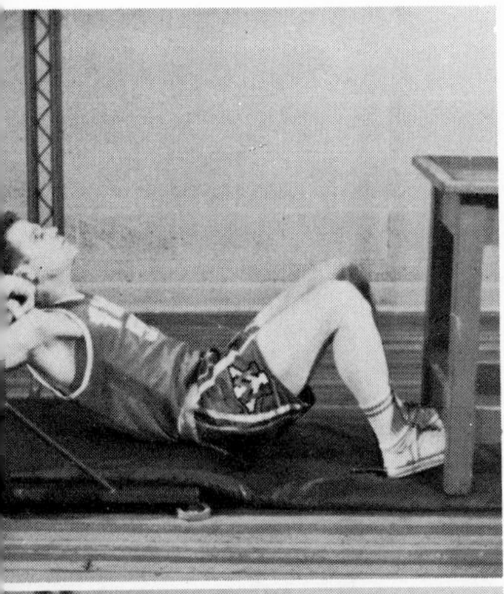

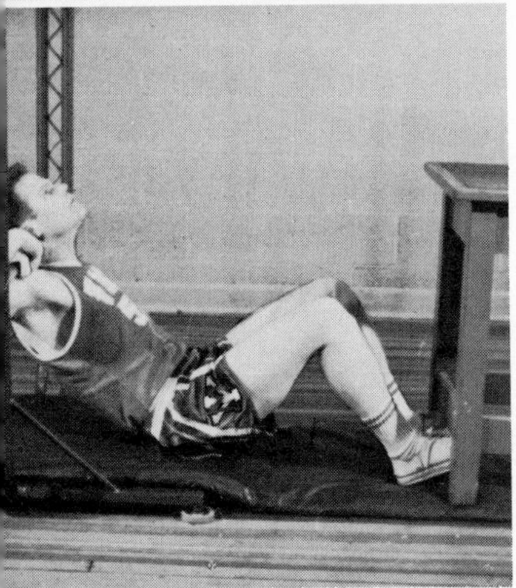

EXERCISE 14

SIT-UPS (LEGS FLEXED)

Coaching Points:

The technique involved is similar to that in Exercise 13, except that the knees are flexed in this exercise. The fact that the knees are in this position will enable the athlete to develop additional musculature not involved in straight leg sit-ups.

Bar Height:

1. Performer's head six inches from the floor.
2. Performer's head twelve inches from the floor.
3. Performer's head eighteen inches from the floor.

Benefits:

FOOTBALL: Instead of developing only the rectus abdominus (above the waist) this exercise includes the iliopsoas (below the waist), providing the athlete with greater protection in this area during contact.

BASKETBALL: General development insures a wholly conditioned athlete.

BASEBALL: Same as above.

EXERCISE 15

SPREAD EAGLE PUSH-UPS

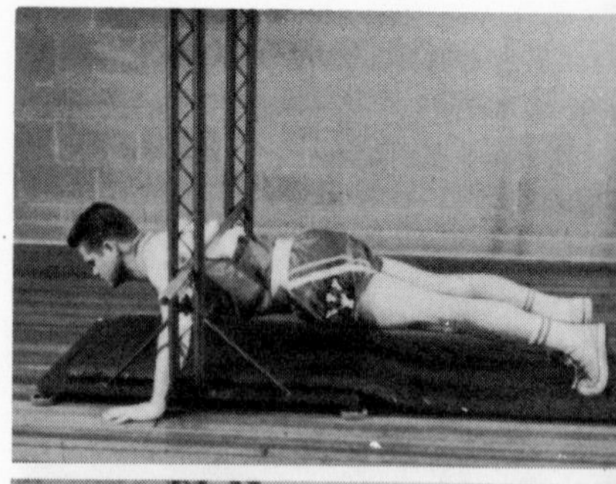

Coaching Points:

The bar should be extremely well padded so that comfort is assured. The arms are fairly widespread, and the attempt is to complete a push-up against the resistance of the bar.

Bar Height:

1. Arms flexed at about 70°.
2. Arms flexed at about 100°.
3. Arms flexed at about 150°.

Benefits:

FOOTBALL: Good developer of shoulder and chest musculature used in forearm shiver and hand fighting essential in line play.

BASKETBALL: General developer and deepener of chest. Musculature involved provides greater power and strength in shooting and passing.

BASEBALL: Development of arm and chest muscles provides more power and greater distance for throwing.

CHAPTER TEN

The Shoulder and Neck

The anatomical areas dealt with in this chapter are each important in athletics, but for different reasons.

The Shoulder

In the case of the shoulder, we are cognizant of the obvious benefits which may be derived through its development. Virtually all of the athletic activities engaged in by man, (with the exception of track and possibly soccer) require the use of the various capabilities of this joint. We pass, throw, put, hurl, press and swing a variety of objects because of it. We raise, lower, adduct, abduct and circumduct our upper extremities through its use. The importance of the shoulder in athletic endeavor certainly may not be seriously questioned.

Our emphasis on the shoulder in our conditioning programs will reap large benefits as the season progresses. As a result of added strength, the demands placed upon it will be accomplished with less effort. Then too, since our players will have to exert less effort in order to accomplish the movements required of this area in sports, they will be able to perform these more efficiently for a longer period of time.

Our purpose in shoulder development then, is one of gaining added strength in order to function more effectively in athletics.

The Neck

A purpose slightly different than that involving the shoulder should underlie our efforts to strengthen the neck. Neck movement is of course desirable, but I would say that it is not *the* most important consideration relative to athletics. My opinion is that we need the maximum degree of *support* and *safety* in this area.

We have often heard of "the typical neck of the contact sport athlete." The statement implies that because a boy plays a contact sport, his neck becomes stronger. In most cases, this is not the whole story. I feel that body development because of hereditary factors sometimes indicates that the individual might be most ably suited to play a contact sport, so he plays. In my experience, I would say that a minority of football conditioning programs include any exercises that might be instrumental in developing the strength of the neck. I consider "bridging" an excellent means of increasing and maintaining the flexibility of the neck, but inadequate as a developer of strength.

Why is strength so important here? Because our techniques in football relative to blocking and tackling make the head and neck a veritable battering ram . . . in effect, a piston. We coach our boys to "follow the face-mask" into the block and the tackle, and this is probably the most effective technique. This being true, then we owe it to our team members to make the neck one of the strongest areas in the body. In order to expect the head and neck to absorb the shocks and blows we expect of it, we cannot trust to normal maturation to achieve the required strength. Safety and injury prevention are two prime considerations when we involve the neck in athletics.

This chapter provides the coach with exercises designed to strengthen both the shoulder (for more effective play) and the neck (for injury prevention and safety).

EXERCISE 1

BENT ARM BENCH PULLOVERS

Coaching Points:

The performer should position himself so that the end of the bench contacts him at about the arm-pit level. The arms should be flexed slightly in all positions. The attempt should be to pull the bar to the chest with a forward and upward movement. Keep the feet flat on the floor.

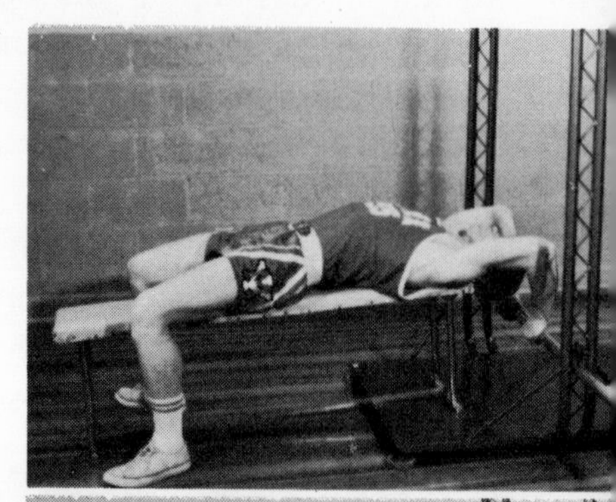

Bar Height:

1. Lowest position the arms can reach and still remain flexed.
2. Even with the height of the bench.
3. Six inches above number 2.

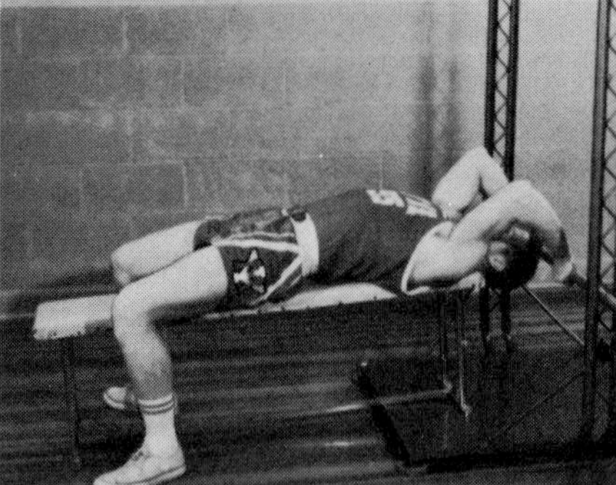

Benefits:

FOOTBALL: Excellent developer of chest strength for linemen. Good exercise to develop the throwing and long snap muscles for quarterbacks and centers.

BASKETBALL: Develops the muscles used in the long pass, jump shooting and set shooting movements.

BASEBALL: Good exercise for both hitters and throwers, but especially the latter. Increase speed and distance in throwing and pitching.

EXERCISE 2

STRAIGHT ARM BENCH PULLOVERS

Coaching Points:

The performer should position himself so that the entire shoulder and head areas are on the bench. He then reaches back for the bar, keeping the arms straight. The attempt should be to pull the bar upward and forward until the bar is directly over the body. Caution the athletes to warm up especially well for this one, and to work up to their contraction very *gradually.*

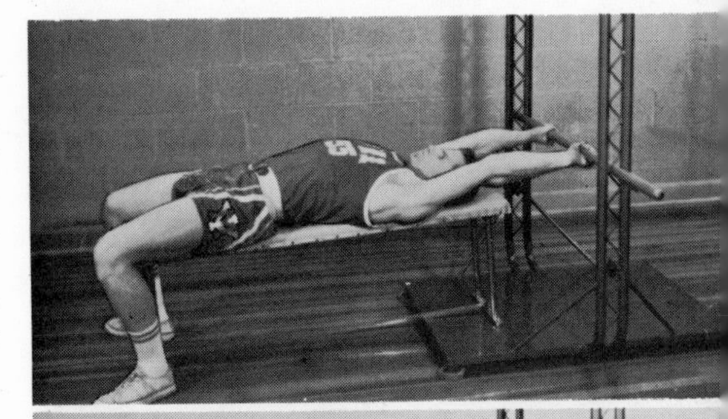

Bar Height:

1. Even with the bench.
2. Arms at 45° angle.
3. Arms at point just before a 90° angle.

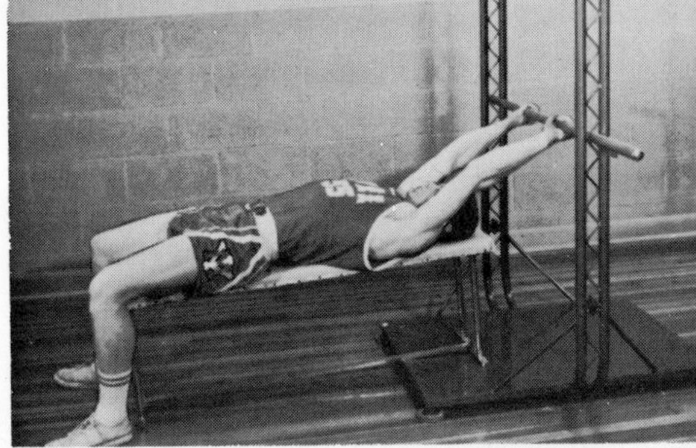

Benefits:

FOOTBALL: This exercise is a must for football players. It not only develops the anterior part of the shoulder for arm tackles, straight-arming, and throwing and snapping; but also increases the range of motion of the shoulder joint to aid in preventing injuries.

BASKETBALL: Increases power and distance in jump shooting, one hand push, and set shots. Increases mobility of joint.

BASEBALL: Increased distance and power in throwing. Increased motion will help to prevent sore arms.

EXERCISE 3

SHOULDER SHRUG

Coaching Points:

Coaching technique is very important here. The performer must be made to understand that the attempted elevation of the bar should be accomplished with the shoulders alone, and not with the arms. Keep the elbows locked, and attempt to raise the shoulders to their highest point.

Bar Height:

1. Lowest point to which the arms can reach without bending forward.
2. Three to four inches above number 1.

Benefits:

FOOTBALL: The deltoid provides a natural shoulder pad for the body, and this exercise develops it, along with other muscles necessary for protection in this area.

BASKETBALL: Helps to develop muscles used in defensive movements of the arms. Helps to prevent fatigue in this area.

BASEBALL: Develops musculature used in hitting, especially involving low balls in the strike zone.

EXERCISE 4

MANUAL NECK ISOMETRICS

Coaching Points:

These exercises are conducted without the use of a rack. A towel or strap may be used, but results are just as good simply using the hands. In 4 A the pull is upward, in 4 B it is backward. 4 C should be repeated to the opposite side. Resist the push or pull of the hands with the neck muscles.

Bar Height:

Not applicable.

Benefits:

FOOTBALL: These exercises will strengthen the neck on all sides, insuring greater safety and less injury to this area as a result of contact. The exercise should be conducted daily, since it requires little time and no equipment.

BASKETBALL: General development.

BASEBALL: General development.

EXERCISE 5

LATERAL RAISES (SUPINE)

Coaching Points:

The performer's whole trunk should be on the bench. The feet should be flat on the floor for stability. The attempt is to raise the bar to a position directly overhead. The palms are down in this particular exercise.

Bar Height:

1. Position to which the arms may reach comfortably without leaning from the bench.
2. Even with the bench height.
3. Arm forming an angle of 45° with the bench.

Benefits:

FOOTBALL: Excellent exercise to develop the deltoid muscle, used in the forearm lift and in the tackling position. Also serves as protection in contact.

BASKETBALL: General shoulder development for all-around strength in rebounding and ball control.

BASEBALL: General shoulder development provides greater power in this area for hitting and throwing. More powerful shoulders mean increased distance in both activities.

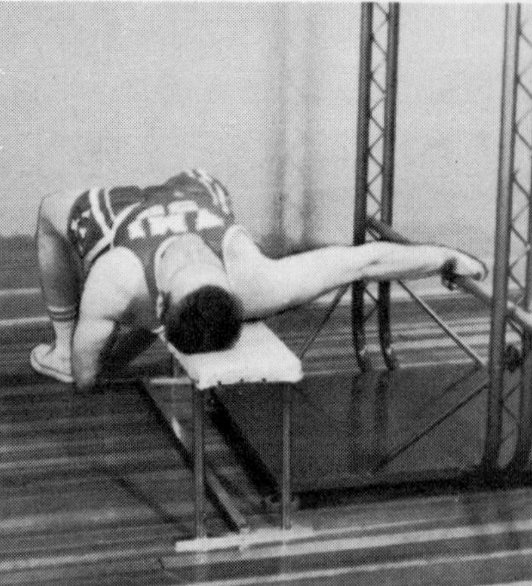

EXERCISE 6

SUPINE REVERSE PULLUPS

Coaching Points:

The performer needs an assist here from a buddy or an immovable object he can hook his feet under. The attempt is to pull the body toward the bar in a straight line.

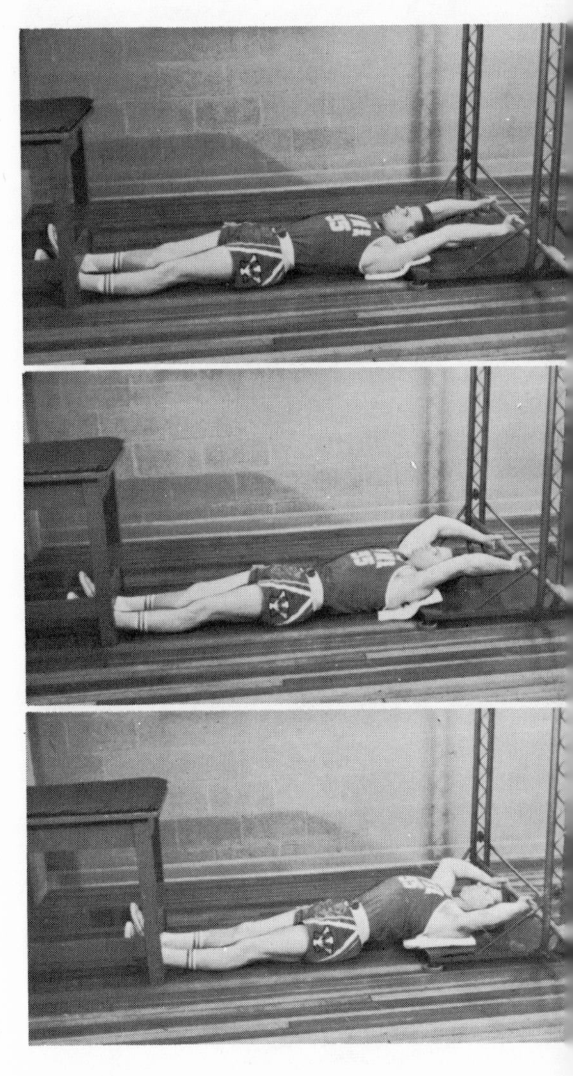

Bar Height:

The bar height remains the same for all positions. The performer adjusts his position so that the arms are extended, flexed to 45° and flexed to about 90°.

Benefits:

FOOTBALL: Increases the power in the shoulder depressors used in "pulling a tackle in", and stabilization in the forearm shiver and hand fighting.

BASKETBALL: Excellent developer of rebounding musculature. (Pulling the ball from the boards with power and increased control.)

BASEBALL: Increase in the strength of the depressors will mean greater power and increased distance in throwing. Will also develop power in the lead arm used in the hitting swing.

EXERCISE 7

POWER CLEAN EXERCISE

Coaching Points:

This exercise is a modification of the method used in "cleaning" a barbell. The first position requires a wide base, hands well spread, with the back at a 45° angle. The attempt is made to lift the bar as high as possible, while maintaining a palms-down position of the hands. In the third position, the performer should be fully extended and up on the toes.

Bar Height:

1. Lowest position on the rack.
2. Stomach level.
3. Nose level.

Benefits:

FOOTBALL: A multiple exercise which develops legs, shoulders and arms. Excellent development of deltoids, needed in blocking and tackling. Commensurate benefit in the extensors of the leg for firing out of the stance.

BASKETBALL: General shoulder and leg development means greater power and control in rebounding, and aids in defensive movements.

BASEBALL: Fine exercise to develop the shoulder musculature involved in throwing and hitting. Development of extensors of legs is an added benefit.

EXERCISE 8

DUMMY NECK COMPRESSOR

Coaching Points:

In the first position, the top of the head should contact the dummy. The arms are locked around it, and the attempt is to force the head into the dummy as far as possible. The second position involves flexing the neck and contacting the dummy with the back of the head. The attempt here is to force in and up, trying to straighten the neck to its original position.

Bar Height:

Not applicable.

Benefits:

FOOTBALL: The benefits here are easily demonstrated by the exercise itself. Development of the neck musculature will allow a boy to be more aggressive in blocking and tackling. Using the second position will aid in preventing forced flexion injuries resulting from contact.

BASKETBALL: General development.

BASEBALL: General development.

EXERCISE 9

BAR BREAKER

Coaching Points:

An alternate grip is assumed on the bar. The hand with the palm facing forward should push in that direction. The hand facing backward should be forcing backward. The position of the hands is reversed for position 9 B.

Bar Height:

May vary with each workout for variety, but should always be above the shoulders. In our photos here, the arms are almost fully extended.

Benefits:

FOOTBALL: Good exercise for quarterbacks, since the throwing or passing muscles are developed. Linemen will benefit through the development of pushing or hand fighting musculature. Assists in shedding blockers.

BASKETBALL: Fine exercise to develop the shoulder muscles used in long passing, push or bounce passing, hook shooting, and jump shooting.

BASEBALL: Development of the depressors and rotators will mean added distance and power in throwing for all fielders. This exercise will also be of value to hitters in that it works on musculature used in pivoting during the swing.

EXERCISE 10

QUARTER-SQUAT REVERSE PULL-THROUGH

Coaching Points:

The performer assumes a quarter-squat position. The arms are relatively straight in position 10 A. The attempt is to pull the bar forward and downward in 10 A and 10 B, and forward and upward in 10 C.

Bar Height:

1. Waist level.
2. Buttocks level.
3. Thigh level.

Benefits:

FOOTBALL: Develops the shoulder and chest musculature used in delivery of the initial blow in the line, pitching out for quarterbacks, and the initial contact in tackling for all defensive personnel.

BASKETBALL: Develops speed and power in underhand and underarm passing. Develops musculature necessary for better ball control in dribbling and tie-up situations.

BASEBALL: Good exercise to develop speed and power in underarm and snap throws. Shoulder and chest development will mean more power and distance in hitting.

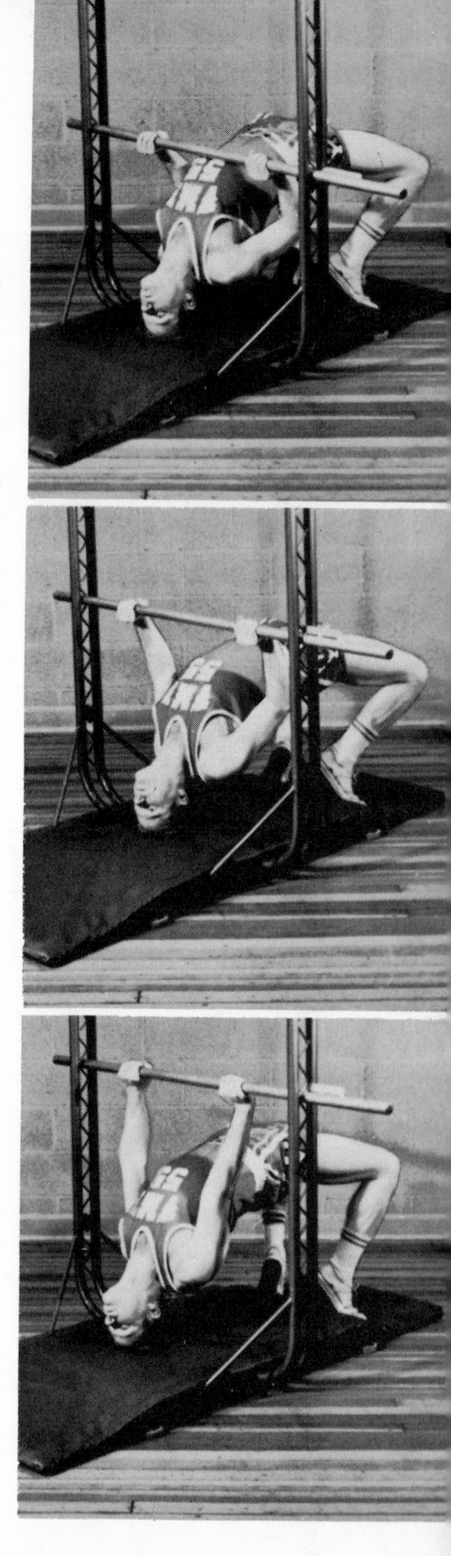

EXERCISE 11

WRESTLER'S BRIDGE AND PRESS

Coaching Points:

Now we are going to make use of a favorite exercise, but with a modification. Now resistance is added to the bridge, making the neck support the body with added weight. The attempt is to force the bar upward with a regular press, while maintaining the arched position of the bridge. The head should be well protected by performing with a mat.

Bar Height:

1. Just above the chest.
2. Arms at 90°.
3. Arms almost fully extended.

Benefits:

FOOTBALL: Another multiple exercise. Develops not only the neck, essential in making authoritative contact in blocking and tackling, but the arms as well. This two-fold exercise aids in developing straight-arming and hand fighting musculature. Probably the greatest benefit is in the aspect of safety and injury prevention in the neck and shoulder areas.

BASKETBALL: General development of the neck, along with development of shooting and passing muscles.

BASEBALL: General development of the neck. Increase in power and distance in throwing.

EXERCISE 12

DOUBLE FOREARM LIFT

Coaching Points:

The arms should be flexed to the angle at which they are generally used in a blocking position. The actual movement of the extension of the legs and trunk should be used, so that in 12 A the performer's legs are flexed as if he has just made contact with an opponent. In 12 B, he is starting to "lift the block," etc. The bar may be padded for comfort.

Bar Height:

1. Waist level.
2. Chest level.
3. Shoulder level.

Benefits:

FOOTBALL: An excellent all-around exercise which develops all of the musculature used in making a one-on-one block. Concentration on the shoulders and arms means more power and less chance of injury.

BASKETBALL: General development of shoulders, arms and legs. More power in going up for the rebound, more control when the ball is secured. Development of shoulders for defensive play and injury prevention.

BASEBALL: General development of shoulders and legs for more power in batting.

EXERCISE 13

ANTERIOR LIFT-CURL

Coaching Points:

The bar must be padded for this exercise, since the point of contact with the bar is at the crook of the elbow. The attempt should be to "curl" the bar as in the normal movement, except that in this case the shoulder muscles are the prime movers.

Bar Height:

1. Close to the body and at stomach level.
2. Chest level.
3. Shoulder level.

Benefits:

FOOTBALL: Development of shoulders and arms to increase force of contact in blocking and tackling. Also will aid in prevention of injury to the shoulder.

BASKETBALL: Development of shoulder musculature used in underhand shooting and passing. Aid in prevention of shoulder injury.

BASEBALL: Development of anterior portion of shoulder will incerase efficiency in throwing. Batting musculature of shoulder will also benefit.

EXERCISE 14

CIRCLE EXERCISE

Coaching Points:

The arms are extended. The performer grasps the bar in a palms-up position. The attempt should be made to lift the bar outward with both hands. In effect, the performer should describe a half-circle with his hands in an upward motion. The hands may be turned to a palms-down position for variety.

Bar Height:

1. Buttocks level.
2. Stomach level.
3. Chest level.

Benefits:

FOOTBALL: Excellent exercise for forearm lift and tackling musculature. Also will aid in stabilizing the shoulder in the blocking position to help prevent injuries.

BASKETBALL: General development of shoulder girdle. Will aid in developing hook shooting distance and power. Good development of musculature used in defensive guarding position.

BASEBALL: General shoulder strength for increased power in hitting, especially relative to the lead arm in the swing.

EXERCISE 15

SUITCASE LIFT

Coaching Points:

In this exercise, no attempt should be made to lean away from the bar as in Side Benders. The attempt is to lift the bar directly up the side, keeping the bar in close proximity to the body. The exercise should be repeated with the alternate arm.

Bar Height:

1. Thigh level.
2. Waist level.
3. Chest level.

Benefits:

FOOTBALL: Excellent exercise to develop the deltoids, essential in "lifting a tackle," the initial contact in a forearm lift, and stabilization of the shoulder to aid in preventing injury resulting from any form of contact.

BASKETBALL: General development of musculature essential in defensive position used in guarding. More powerful shoulders will aid in controlling the ball in rebounding. This exercise will assist in developing the muscles that stabilize the shoulder when the arms are fully extended.

BASEBALL: More powerful shoulders to aid in generating strength and speed in the batting swing. Deltoids will also aid in increasing power and distance in throwing.

APPENDIX

Exercises for Additional Sports

Because of space limitations, only those sports normally considered as "major" were discussed in connection with the exercises presented in chapters six through ten.

In the following section, sports and activities other than the "big" three" are considered.

As you will note, twenty to thirty exercises are suggested for most sports. To employ all of them at one time in a conditioning program would be impossible and impractical. The list of possibilities is meant only as a guide for the coach.

Once the decision to include isometrics in the training program has been made, the coach should examine the list relative to his particular interest carefully. All of the activities have been analyzed, and only those exercises which are pertinent have been included in the chart.

It is suggested that a selection of fifteen or sixteen exercises be chosen from the total list for use in a program. This selection should be further broken down to a basic list of nine or ten "core" exercises. These should be accomplished on each workout day. The remaining exercises may be used to supplement those in the "core." In this way, the conditioning program may be kept interesting and flexible.

Use the following charts only as a guide, keeping in mind your own special personnel problems and situation.

Make your selection on the basis of the chapters covering the various areas of the body, making certain that enough are included to cover each aspect or area thoroughly.

BOWLING

CHAPTER SIX
Exercises: 1, 3, 4, 6, 9, 10, 13.

CHAPTER SEVEN
Exercises: 6, 7, 15.

CHAPTER EIGHT
Exercises: 1, 2, 5, 6, 13.

CHAPTER NINE
Exercises: 1, 5, 6, 10,
11, 13 or 14.

CHAPTER TEN
Exercises: 3, 5, 9, 10, 13, 15.

DIVING

CHAPTER SIX
Exercises: 7, 8, 11, 14.

CHAPTER SEVEN
Exercises: 1, 3, 6, 7, 12, 13, 14, 15, 17.

CHAPTER EIGHT
Exercises: 2, 7, 12, 13.

CHAPTER NINE
Exercises: 7, 9, 10, 11, 12, 13, 14.

CHAPTER TEN
Exercises: 1, 2, 15.

GOLF

CHAPTER SIX
Exercises: 1, 2, 3, 4, 6, 9, 10, 13

CHAPTER SEVEN
Exercises: 3, 4, 5, 13.

CHAPTER EIGHT
Exercises: 1, 3, 10, 13, 16 (converted to golf swing).

CHAPTER NINE
Exercises :2, 5, 10, 11, 13 or 14.

CHAPTER TEN
Exercises: 3, 9, 14 15.

HOCKEY

CHAPTER SIX
Exercises: 1, 2, 3, 4, 6, 9, 10, 11, 13.

HOCKEY (cont.)

CHAPTER SEVEN
Exercises: 1, 2, 3, 4, 5, 6, 7, 13, 14, 15.

CHAPTER EIGHT
Exercises: 1, 3, 7, 12, 13, 15.

CHAPTER NINE
Exercises: 1, 5, 6, 7, 8, 10, 11, 13 or 14.

CHAPTER TEN
Exercises: 2, 3, 5, 7, 9, 10, 15.

SKIING

CHAPTER SIX
Exercises: 3, 9.

CHAPTER SEVEN
Exercises: 1, 2, 3, 4, 5, 6, 7, 13, 14, 15, 17.

CHAPTER EIGHT
Exercises: 1, 7, 12, 13.

CHAPTER NINE
Exercises: 7, 9, 10, 11, 12, 13 or 14.

CHAPTER TEN
Exercises: 7, 9, 15.

SOCCER

CHAPTER SIX
Exercises: 8, 9, 14.

CHAPTER SEVEN
Exercises: 1, 2, 3, 4, 5, 6, 7, 8, 9, 11, 13, 14, 15.

SOCCER (cont.)

CHAPTER EIGHT
Exercises: 1, 7, 12, 13.

CHAPTER NINE
Exercises: 7, 9, 10, 11, 12, 13 or 14.

CHAPTER TEN
Exercises: 4, 8, 9, 15.

SWIMMING

CHAPTER SIX
Exercises: 1, 3, 8, 9, 11.

CHAPTER SEVEN
Exercises: 2, 4, 5, 8, 10, 13, 14, 17.

CHAPTER EIGHT
Exercises: 3, 4, 6, 8, 12, 13, 17.

CHAPTER NINE
Exercises: 1, 4, 5, 7, 9, 10, 11, 12, 13 or 14.

CHAPTER TEN
Exercises: 1, 5, 6, 7, 10, 13, 15.

TENNIS

CHAPTER SIX
Exercises: 3, 4, 6, 8, 9, 10, 11, 12, 13.

CHAPTER SEVEN
Exercises: 2, 3, 4, 5, 6, 15.

CHAPTER EIGHT
Exercises: 1, 3, 12, 14, 16 (converted to tennis stroke).

TENNIS (*cont.*)

CHAPTER NINE
Exercises: 1, 5, 8, 10, 11, 13 or 14.

CHAPTER TEN
Exercises: 1, 2, 9, 14, 15.

TRACK—(FIELD EVENTS)

CHAPTER SIX
Exercises: 1, 2, 3, 4, 5, 6, 7, 8, 9, 10, 11, 12, 13, 14.

CHAPTER SEVEN
Exercises: 3, 4, 7, 12, 13, 14, 16.

CHAPTER EIGHT
Exercises: 1, 3, 4, 5, 7, 9, 13, 15, 17.

CHAPTER NINE
Exercises: 1, 2, 3, 4, 5, 6, 8, 10, 11, 12, 13 or 14, 15.

CHAPTER TEN
Exercises: 1, 2, 3, 5, 6, 7, 9, 10, 11, 12, 13, 14, 15.

TRACK—(RUNNING EVENTS)

CHAPTER SIX
Exercises: 8, 9, 10.

CHAPTER SEVEN
Exercises: 1 or 2, 3, 4, 5, 6, 7, 8, 13, 14, 15.

CHAPTER EIGHT
Exercises: 7, 12, 13.

TRACK—RUNNING EVENTS (cont.)

CHAPTER NINE
Exercises: 4, 7, 9, 12, 13 or 14.

CHAPTER TEN
Exercises: 1, 2, 3.

WRESTLING

CHAPTER SIX
Exercises: 1, 2, 3, 4, 5, 6, 7, 8, 9, 10, 13, 14.

CHAPTER SEVEN
Exercises: 4, 5, 7, 10, 12, 13, 14, 16, 17.

CHAPTER EIGHT
Exercises: 1, 2, 3, 4, 5, 6, 7, 8, 9, 10, 12, 13, 14, 15, 16.

CHAPTER NINE
Exercises: 1, 2, 3, 4, 6, 7, 9, 10, 11, 12, 13, 14, 15.

CHAPTER TEN
Exercises: 1, 2, 3, 4, 5, 6, 7, 8, 9, 10, 11, 12, 13, 14, 15.